THE EARTH CHANGERS

OTHER BOOKS BY THE SAME AUTHORS

JOINTLY:
>   *Southern Pacific:* The Roaring Story of a Fighting Railroad

BY NEILL C. WILSON:
>   *The Freedom Song,* a novel
>   *The Nine Brides and Granny Hite,* a novel
>   *Treasure Express:* Epic Days of the Wells Fargo
>   *Silver Stampede:* The Story of Death Valley's Hell-Camp, Old Panamint

BY FRANK J. TAYLOR:
>   *Black Bonanza*
>   (with Earl M. Welty)
>   *High Horizons*
>   *"Oh, Ranger!"*
>   (with Horace M. Albright)

The
Earth Changers

NEILL C. WILSON and FRANK J. TAYLOR

1957 DOUBLEDAY & COMPANY, INC., GARDEN CITY, N.Y.

To the rugged construction stiff in his hard hat and muddy boots, doing his best, and doing it well, from Arctic Circle to Antarctic and from Suez right around to Suez. Teaching what he knows to distant peoples, and learning from them considerably more than he teaches. May he come home safe and sound to the wife and kids.

FOREWORD

BECAUSE Hoover Dam opened a new era of heavy construction on all continents, and because the covers of this book are only a few hundred pages apart, the writers have concentrated this chronicle on some of the Six who built Hoover. From that mighty dam of the '30s those builders and their sons went on to present-day achievements that are on a world-wide scale.

The book is not an encyclopedia. It is only a sampling. It does not include all the engineers and builders who are currently reshaping portions of the earth. It does not do justice to nor even name all the firms, designers, managers, superintendents, and foremen who construct dams, pipelines, refineries; who hew tunnels and vitalize deserts.

Authors and publisher alike wish to emphasize that this is an unsponsored, independent review of the companies concerned. In this study the engineering, construction, and financial facts were obtained with the valued co-operation of those chiefly involved, and whose work is described; but all conclusions, observations, and points of view are independently presented. This is not a "company book."

The Erlander, Lloyd, Quinn, and Kanterwitz families, Pepe and Jorge Pilar, Qadi Bahr and Yadiah Ghaylan are improvisations, supplied to give the common man his place in a story of rivers being turned, steel erected, concrete poured, and mountains moved.

All other persons mentioned or described are flesh and blood members of the legion of doers who are making a new kind of history. Ambassadors of private enterprise, they are giving American business a new dimension, and are winning the respect of peoples everywhere.

NEILL C. WILSON
FRANK J. TAYLOR

CONTENTS

THE EARTH CHANGERS

1

THE SPRINGBOARD

THE YEAR was 1930 and crops were abundant, but men were starving. And men could have stood that, for a while. But what drove them desperate was seeing their wives and children in want. Everywhere it was the same: in Texas, New York, Oregon; in West Virginia, where Art Lloyd's people had been coal miners for generations; in Minnesota, where Olof Erlander was a house painter. Dismay and disaster on such a scale didn't seem possible, in America. But Art knew them for facts when the coal trains went off with their last loads and the mines shut down. And Olof realized it when he was paid off and told, "That's all."

"For a veek?" asked Olof.

"For months, Olof, as far as I can tell," the boss said. "The country has gone bust. Don't ask me why."

It was September, and Minnesota's lakes are lovely in September. Olof, a rangy, muscular man of thirty-seven, went fishing. October was even more beautiful, but the fun had gone out of fishing. By December, Olof knew he was in deep trouble. His wife showed him what was left of their cash. "Ve got to do something, Olof. T'ink of something." Tooe had been plump and cute when Olof married her. Now she was no longer plump, and too tired to be cute.

Minnesota's snow was eaves-high, would stay banked high until spring. Everyone in Hibbing was used to living on credit when winter closed the iron mines. But what would old Hedtoft do to restock his store if the mines didn't reopen? What would the Erlanders and their neighbors do for groceries, for coal?

Olof heard something on the radio. President Hoover's government had decided to spend a hundred and sixty million dollars fixing up the Colorado River, wherever that was, with a powerhouse and canals and a dam.

"A hundred and sixty thousand dollars!" echoed Tooe.

"Million dollars," corrected Olof.

"All that!" revised Tooe. She went on mending Molly's red jumper dress with her stubby hands.

One million or 160 million, it was a lot. (Off in West Virginia, Art and Shana Lloyd were saying much the same thing.)

Olof and Tooe packed up their Model T, and when it was overflowing with household gear they stuffed in Peter, Molly, Winona, Carl, Magnus, and themselves.

"Where, now, is this Colorado River?" asked Tooe.

"It's in Nevada, next to Arizona."

"And where are Nevada and Arizona?"

"Down by California someplace, ay hear, where it's sunny and varm."

Half of Hibbing, Minnesota, was on its way and the Erlanders fell in with the rusty parade. From every corner of the country families hungry and cold, families sick and worried, were streaking for the Colorado and a part, any part, of that golden rain of $160 million. Olof Erlander of Minnesota and Art Lloyd of West Virginia didn't know each other yet. But, come a day, they would meet.

Far out on the southwestern desert they found that river, and it was like nothing they'd ever seen before. "It's so small!" said Tooe, looking over the edge. "Maybe she's vay down," said Olof, who was used to painters' scaffolds and high places. "There are no trees," said Molly. "Papa, where are the trees?" All was sand and stone.

They went into a squatters' camp, not knowing when the work would begin, but Olof was determined to be on hand. They and their neighbors from Hibbing, the Quinns and Kanterwitzes, made their homes in their cars or in shacks knocked up out of tar paper and boxes. They located near the only water they could find, a trickle in a stony gully, and when that turned bitter they went down by a steep route Olof discovered and dipped from the river. That water was brackish, too, and brown with sand; the river carried as much silt as a fully loaded train of gondola cars moving at five miles an hour, forever. This was the river that had sawed the Grand Canyon down a mile below its rims, and the Grand was only one of many such canyons it had sawed.

During 1930's fall and winter two hundred babies were born in the rag and tar village, and Tooe Erlander and Shana Lloyd, among the half-thousand women living in Tar Town, did their best to help the new mothers, although they had their own broods to feed or to comfort when food ran low. As it did. But there was a little work for the menfolk and Olof found his share—stake driving and rod holding.

The region was very cold—the dry cold of the desert. Even in Minnesota, Tooe and Olof had known no stinging cold like this. Sometimes there were high winds, too. Roofs sailed off into the air. And the winds brought dust. If a dry wind sifted one pailful of dust into a closed shack, it was a "one-bucketer" gale. Often there were two-bucketers and three-bucketers. Tooe and Molly, their legs bare and wind-cracked, their blond braids tied with bits of colored rag, vexedly cleaned up the mess.

Tooe thought of the lovely snowdrifts that used to hold everything down in winter, burying the red iron mines. "You and your warm, sunny desert," she said to Olof.

"You yust vait," retorted Olof.

During a dust storm another event happened in the Erlander cabin. Tooe and Olof's fourth son was born in the midst of a three-bucketer, while Shana Lloyd and Moira Kanterwitz assisted.

The refugees learned something about the river they'd come here to dam. It rose in the snowfields of the Rockies up in Colorado and Wyoming. In 1,700 miles it tumbled 14,000 feet. In late spring its rapids could roar with 100,000 or 200,000 cubic feet of water a second; in December, when its high Rocky Mountain sources were frozen, it skipped down its staircases with a mere 3,000 or 4,000 second-feet. It was a peculiar stream, full of circular and side eddies and sudden fountains or "boils"; and when rainstorms hit the treeless country far above, it doubled in size without warning, humping itself like a cat's back. Much of its course lay in a tremendously deep trough. But long miles south of Black Canyon, which was the name of the gorge below Tar Town, the side walls fell away and for part of its final run to the Gulf of California the river moved between sandy dikes of its own making, dikes further bolstered up by man. At one point the river was actually above the desert which farmers had made into lush Imperial Valley. In times past the settlers in that valley had seen the river come spilling down upon their farms in a Niagara of fury and had battled for their lives. Control of such floods was a prime purpose of the dam that was to be built in Black Canyon. Originally planned for Boulder Canyon, the next narrow place up the stream, it still bore the name Boulder Dam, temporarily.

Tooe and Olof began to hear details of the proposed structure which the Reclamation people had designed. It was to be a concrete arch 726 feet high, with a crest 1,180 feet long, and its base would be 660 feet thick. No dam of such height and grandeur had ever been built. The powerhouse below it would be capable of lighting up a 40-watt bulb for every family in the United States.

Sometimes Tooe and her man and Shana Lloyd and her man and other wives and husbands and a multitude of children trudged out across the chilly desert and looked down into Black Canyon. Its walls were a series of sheer drops and narrow shelves, deeply carved by vertical fissures. This side was in Nevada and the opposite wall was in Arizona. The river was 800 feet below. Down where the coffee-colored river churned, the chasm was 370 feet wide. Here at the top its width was 970 feet. In that narrow slot thousands of men in the months to come would work elbow to elbow, tunneling the walls to take the river around the damsite, cleaning out the bed down to solid rock, and inserting the 6,500,000-ton concrete plug.

The river, draining one-thirteenth of the United States, rolled and stormed with the power of 11 million horses. The dam that would tame that river would create a lake long enough to reach from Seattle to Portland or from Schenectady to New York, and deep enough to lap the Empire State Building up to the sixtieth floor. It was a frightening proposition. Olof Erlander, Tom Quinn, Abe Kanterwitz, and other neighbors old and new often discussed it.

"Such concrete!" said Abe. "It will never be poured."

"It will heat up," said Tom, "and not cool down in a hundred years. When it does cool, it will crack."

"How vill they put it in there?" wondered Olof. "How vill they hold the river back? You can't stand in that river. You can hardly row a boat across it. And this is low water. Ay've seen dead trees—the trash vashed down by floods—sticking to the cliffs fifty feet up. Vat vill happen if such floods come vile ve're vorking?"

"I hear the dam alone will cost fifty, sixty millions," said Abe Kanterwitz. "The contractor will have to give a bond. Who can make such a bond? There won't be any work here for us. I tell my Moira we were crazy to come here."

Olof said to Tooe, "But ve vill stay."

Where else could they go?

Other men kept coming out across the desert to look down into Black Canyon. They usually stood there silently and thoughtfully and then went away. "Contractors," said Abe Kanterwitz to Olof, "thinking about bidding. But they don't want it." Abe had been a small paving contractor, back home in Hibbing.

One day Olof was standing at the rim, wondering once again how men ever dreamed they could plug that chasm, when a car drove up through the greasewood and gravel. Two men got out. One was well over six feet tall, a spare figure who seemed to feel the wind through his tightly wrapped overcoat. But he stood a long while, looking down and off from under the brim of a shabby soft hat with a sweaty band. His eyes roved the leaping stream below; they took in the sheer wall opposite. His lips tightened in an odd grin.

The other man was spare, too, though not so tall. He had a jaw that set like a rock. He, too, held his overcoat against the wind.

"Well, Frank?" asked this second man, the one with the granite chin.

"Well, H.W.?" said the one with the tight, wry grin.

"Can you build it?"

"Of course."

That night, in their Tar Town shack, Olof said to Tooe, "Ay saw the feller today who is going to put the dam down there."

"No man can put the dam down there," said Tooe, who was fed up with everything about this place.

"This feller can," said Olof.

2

THE PARTICIPANTS

IN SAN FRANCISCO an elderly man lay dying. He was a builder, and had been one all his life; he had pierced the West with tunnels and spanned it with rails. He was also a rancher, and the Utah Construction Company he and his brother had put together owned 30,000 cattle and 25,000 sheep on 600,000 acres. But now old W. H. Wattis was faced both with the hour of departure and the moment of decision. His associates wanted him to approve a venture whereby several contractors, each putting up all that could be scraped together, would attempt jointly to build a dam of a size that staggered imagination.

"What does E.O. say?" E.O. was W. H. Wattis's brother. All their lives they'd shared everything. But E.O. too was elderly—he was seventy-six, four years older than W.H.—and also ailing.

"He wants us to build it. Look," said Hank Lawler, Utah's superintendent. Hank, together with rival construction superintendent, Frank Crowe, and contractor, Harry Morrison, had wheeled a working model of the dam into the room in St. Francis Hospital. Morrison was not a Utah Construction

Company man, but he was taking a hand in putting this builder-group together.

"Who else wants to go in? Are they our kind of people?"

Yes, they were W.H.'s kind—dependable, resourceful. They were eight firms in all—three of them coming in as a single unit. Among them they had done about $400 million worth of construction and were currently occupied with $30 million more. They were not amateurs. But they weren't national figures, either.

The government-proposed series of works on the Colorado River had been broken down into manageable units. Starting with the high dam in Black Canyon, it was to be followed with other dams farther downstream. There also were to be plants for generating electricity from the falling water and canals for spreading the life-giving water out over desert acres. The initial job, and the key one, would be that high dam. Nothing of like scope had been offered to private builders before. New York, Chicago, and Baltimore contractors were also interested; they had asked Colonel Jack Savage of the Reclamation Service for specifications and blueprints and were sharpening their pencils.

The man in the hospital bed knew that he would never see the dam finished, or even begun. But it was a glorious gamble, and if the others wanted it his old fighting heart joined in accepting the challenge. "All right, boys, Utah will go in."

Who were these Wattises?

In the gold-rush days in California, eighty years before, an eighteen-year-old named Edmund Wattis had run out of miner's luck and started back for his home in Nebraska. He'd got as far as the eastern side of Great Salt Lake when he found a girl, took up land, and stayed. Two sons of the marriage were Ed and Will, to be known as E.O. and W.H. They were blizzard-bitten country-bred boys of a region where settlers were still pulling arrows out of their walls, and where a roofed-over cellar made a fine house. The boys were taught to root or die. They rooted as a pair. "All I learned in school," remembered E.O. when he'd become a millionaire, "was how to add and subtract, and I learned how to divide by divvying with my brother."

The Union Pacific was being pushed through, Omaha to Utah, in '68. A foreman noticed twelve-year-old E.O. plowing the family farm with a yoke of oxen. He hired the boy to help grade for the oncoming tracks. Whacking bulls for a railroad cut was exactly the same as whacking them for a crop of corn, except that one got paid for it, so the barefoot kid whacked hides for the westward-creeping Overland. Those were exciting days for any intermountain youngster: Irish graders and tracklayers for the Union Pacific hurrying west from the other side of the Rockies, Chinese graders and Irish tracklayers for the Central Pacific hurrying east from California, and the two destined to meet head-on, swinging pick-handles and throwing dynamite, just north of Great Salt Lake. History was being carved in the gravel beds of northern Utah and the boy with the bullocks helped carve it. He never was the same afterward. He was a constructor for life. So in time were his younger brother, his relatives, and all who tied to his shirttail.

At thirteen the boy acquired a span of mules and a wagon. With a couple of farmers he set to hauling freight around Salt Lake to Montello, a twenty-one-day journey. The golden spike was driven in the spring of '69, and forty thousand hell-raising workmen were in the tent camps along the right-of-way. Construction! The biggest excitement in sight except actually running a locomotive! The greatest show on earth!

Further opportunity to watch the show came to E.O. in the form of a job to winter-haul some freight, mainly whisky, to Boise, Idaho. An uncle who was twenty-four joined the enterprise, and the party bucked snow there and back. They got home broke. It had been a wonderful journey.

By '81, E.O. and brother W.H. had a few teams, wagons, and scrapers, and were at it in railroad grading on their own. They subcontracted a stretch in Idaho for the Oregon Short Line, and they joined their uncles, the Coreys, in further ventures. E.O., over six feet and slender, with blue eyes and lots of wavy hair, was the horseflesh expert of the outfit and in the years when his Utah Construction Company became one of the great ranch owners of the West, E.O. passed eye and hand over practically every horse that the outfit bought. Ben Arp, who became a tunnel expert of the company, tells how he saw E.O. ride a horse over an 18-inch trestle stringer, a hundred feet aloft. With the years and Ben's telling, the length of that trestle probably stretched some, but it doesn't matter; E.O. had nerve and could ride. W.H. was heavier-set, shorter than his brother, and a jolly storyteller. The pair had a younger brother, Warren, whom they sent through Cornell. Warren became a constructor, too.

Railroads were being projected all over the open spaces—in Oregon, Idaho, Montana, Calgary, Colorado. The little family company went smash in the panic of '93, but the Wattis brothers paid up. That cramped them, but they'd won the approval of Ogden bankers David Eccles and Tom Dee. W.H. went ahead rebuilding his fortunes as a subcontractor on railroad jobs, while E.O. ran a herd of sheep. In 1900 the brothers organized the Utah Construction Company. In the ensuing fifty-four years it was to do some thumping-big construction feats. It started with $24,000. Additional stock sales, by

1906, increased the capital to $310,000. After that, no stock was sold to the public, a matter which the good people of Utah have been rueful about ever since.

The First National Bank of Ogden handed E.O. a checkbook and told him to use it. E.O. bought horses, harness, and scrapers. These were put to work on the Denver & Rio Grande and the Oregon Short Line. Utah Construction built the Western Pacific's line from Salt Lake City to Oroville, California. It led through scenic Feather River Canyon and involved forty-five tunnels and 725 miles of track, and remains to this day one of the company's chief monuments. The outfit carried on, in New Mexico, in Oregon, and in California where it built ten tunnels for the Southern Pacific. It built the eel-like Northwestern Pacific from Willits to Eureka, a sensational stretch through slide-minded mountains and the dim redwood forests of California's north coast. It took on the dramatic Carizo Gorge of the Arizona Eastern from San Diego to El Centro, cutting and blasting for 20 miles on a canyon wall through especially tough granite. Utah also built the $6 million O'Shaughnessy Dam for San Francisco's high Sierra water supply.

A. H. Christensen, a contractor in Utah in his own name, joined forces with Utah Construction Company shortly after its organization in 1900. He served as a vice-president until his death in 1932. He was responsible for directing much of the construction work in the intermountain area. On the Western Pacific railroad construction from Oroville to Salt Lake, he built the eastern half while E. O. Wattis directed work on the western half. He was in charge of work performed for the Utah Copper Company, now Kennecott, which was the beginning of his company's knowledge of open-pit mining work.

Hoover Dam, upstream view, 1935, lake beginning to fill.

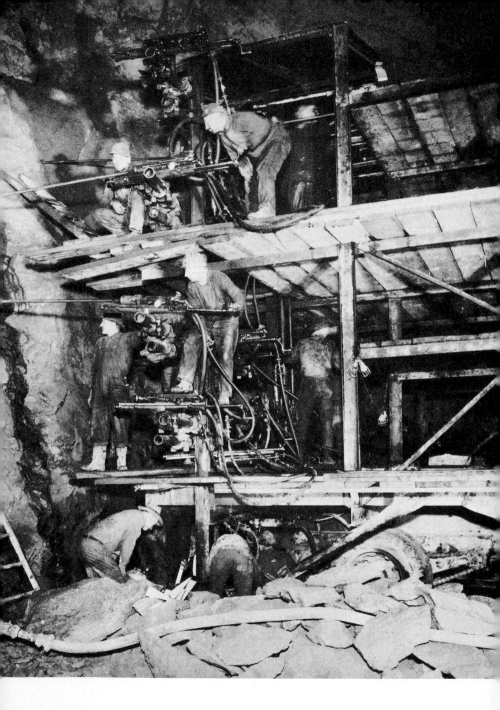

The "Jumbo" that revolutionized tunneling.

Hoover Dam "topped out," late in 1934.

At Hoover in the '30's: H. W. Morrison, Henry J. Kaiser, Frank Crowe, Felix Kahn, Guy Stevick, Gus Ayers, Steve Bechtel.

Scaffolding for bolting a cliff at Hoover and, below, inside the rock-bolting job.

Supply plane wings for Dewline construction camp.

"Small but our own"—home on the Dewline with, below, a call
from the postman.

Huge Dewline cargo trains roll high and wide.

His son, Allen D., heads the Utah Construction Company today.

In 1926, when Sud Pacifico de Mexico was building, there was no heavy constructor in the West as well-heeled or experienced as Utah. It took the Mexican West Coast line through the heavy barranca country and landed it up there on the plateau of the Aztecs. The work on the Southern Pacific's long branch brought forcibly to construction men's attention the differences in temperament between men on the two sides of the border. Early one morning, just after work started, a couple of natives came by, each with a fighting cock under his arm. The whole crew quit work for the cockfight. This happened frequently, to the anguish of Hank Lawler, a forceful driver of the old school who was bossing matters Mexican in the early stages. But in the dark hours one night he left with haste on a motor-driven speed car, just ahead of a group of employees who didn't agree with Hank's desire to get the work done quickly. That brought to the jobsite Lester S. Corey, who'd started with the organization in 1900 as timekeeper. He became Utah's general manager in '31, its president in '40, and is still its elder statesman.

With construction jobs scattered all over the West, Utah in the 1920s subcontracted many portions. One of the firms well liked by E.O. and W.H. was Morrison-Knudsen of Boise, Idaho. The Guernsey Dam on the North Platte in Wyoming came up for bidding. When Harry Morrison proposed that M-K and Utah bid jointly on the venture, the Wattises fell in line. Everybody made money, and the stage was set for something bigger.

W. A. Bechtel, whose firm was prominent in the Black Canyon project, drove into the western construction scene in 1898

down in Indian Territory, behind a span of mules. He'd been
forced out of Peabody, Kansas, where his father ran a grocery,
by droughts and the money panic of the nineties. Rails were
being laid in the Indian country, and any man with a strong
pair of mules could find work there. Bèchtel was hired on the
spot. He followed his slip-scraper thereafter to Indiana, Iowa,
Minnesota, and wild-west Wyoming where Harriman was
rearranging the Union Pacific Railroad. Then to Oregon, as a
gang foreman for the Southern Pacific; Nevada, where he
landed with a wife, two babies, and a ten-dollar bill and a
slide trombone. He found a job as estimator at the railroad
village of Wadsworth. He picked up two friendships there
which endured: V. G. Hindmarsh, someday vice-president of
Bechtel Corporation, and George S. Colley, father of International Bechtel's future president, George S. Colley, Jr. From
Wadsworth, W. A. Bechtel moved on to Lovelock, Nevada,
where he operated a gravel pit for the railroad and lived with
his growing family in a boxcar, and where his kid brother,
Art, perched out on the boom of a steam shovel and operated
the bucket trip with a jerk rope.

In 1904 Bechtel moved to Oakland, California, and went
to work for a local paving firm. When San Francisco went
up in flames in 1906, the Bechtel family was at Placerville,
California, the once-famous Hangtown of the gold days,
where Bechtel operated a slate quarry for the Oakland pavers.
From that he went into business for himself. George Colley,
Sr., went with him for the ride.

The pair subcontracted a Western Pacific job from Utah
Construction Company east of San Francisco Bay, ran into
heavily overbreaking limestone, did some persuasive holler-
ing about more pay for the excess digging, and made a little
money. Here Bechtel also acquired a steam shovel. With his

name proudly painted on it, he dug and shoveled northward through various jobs. In Oregon he ran into Heinie Hindmarsh again. That veteran of the Wadsworth days was resident engineer for the Southern Pacific. Bechtel took out a couple of cuts on the railroad's new extension from Eugene eastward, working the job in his shirtsleeves. The prime contractor was Utah Construction Company.

W.A. was by then "Dad" Bechtel to all. He was gentle and kindly, but he hadn't skinned mules for nothing. In emergencies he could lift his voice the length of a job, and send the bears climbing trees. A solid, thick-chested, dependable man, he was known as a subcontractor who did his work on time and kept his equipment up, and as a boss who operated a good cookhouse. Irrigation and railroad jobs followed in California; a piece of railroad construction in Utah; and successive camps along the Northwestern Pacific lines in California. Dad had capable men about him. They included his brother Art, George Colley, Sr., and Al Berlander, who later would help push an oil pipeline clear across Arabia as Bechtel construction manager. In and about the camps were his three sons: Warren, who was fourteen when the NWP work started; Steve, twelve; Kenneth, eight. Their playmates on boxcar and steam shovel were George Colley, Jr., and his brother, Wallace.

Trucks began replacing horses on the NWP job. And the three Bechtel sons, growing up, began to take over.

In the early twenties the Southern Pacific started in earnest to finish a new route between Oregon and California. The 270-mile link of the Cascade Line, Natron to Black Butte, was built by Utah, and Warren Bechtel subbed a part of that with Dad's backing. He, too, tried something new: tracklaying-type tractors. He brought the newfangled agricultural ma-

chinery up from California and put it to work for the railroad.
Steve Bechtel, Dad's second son, after a stretch as project
chief on a Southern Pacific main-line extension into Phoenix,
came up from Arizona and plunged into the Cascade construction. He built retaining walls, culverts, and viaducts, and
applied the firm's first diesel-powered shovel to his part of the
job. Thirty years later that 50-B Bucyrus was still shoveling,
in an Oroville rock plant that used to be owned by Dad
Bechtel and a party named Henry Kaiser.

Dad had become experienced at going it alone or in temporary fifty-fifty partnerships sealed with a handshake. But
in 1925 he went fancy, incorporating himself, his sons, and
his brother Art as W. A. Bechtel Co.—the name that had been
fancifully painted on his first power shovel sixteen years before. There was lots of work: train sheds, snow sheds in
the Sierra Nevada, a 20,000-foot water tunnel on which the
Bechtels lost their shirts, and a big irrigation dam high in the
Sierra, only thirty miles from the old California mining town
of Grass Valley in an air line, but so remote from civilization
by road that everything used in the camp had to be brought
in before Christmas—not to be replaced again until snow
melted in April. "Everything" meant just that, including a
hundred head of cattle for the cookhouse platters.

On this undertaking the Bechtels made the acquaintance
of Perry Yates, a young engineer on an adjoining job. He, too,
as the years went on, was folded into the Bechtel staff, to be
heard from later.

Southward, midway up the 14,000-foot Sierra wall, nestled
the Sequoia National Park with its big trees. Kenneth Bechtel
went down there and built the "General's Highway," with
masonry bridges of appropriate beauty in a wildly magnificent setting. To keep blasted rock from hurting the grand

trees, Kenneth put pants of sheet metal on them. It was something new for the 3,000-year-oldsters that thought they had seen everything, but they took their new attire gravely. Presently the Bechtels built their first pipeline, teaming up with Silas Palmer, who had found Dad Bechtel's first job for him in California following the Nevada days. Palmer was a pipeliner from away back—he'd built the Coalinga-Monterey "screw-pipe" line in 1903. The new undertaking was an acetylene-welded gas line for the Pacific Gas & Electric. Steve Bechtel, under Palmer's eye, ran this project and he tossed in something new—the sideboom tractor for lifting and lowering pipe into place instead of the laborious tripod and chain block.

Pipeline No. 2 soon followed—a lengthy one for its time. This was a gas line from Tracy to Crockett in California. It, too, added something—electric welding performed in the field. Number 3 was a 140-mile stretch of a 500-mile, 24-inch Continental Gas line between Amarillo, Texas, and Omaha. The job was done by Bechtel-Kaiser Co., Ltd. The Kaiser in the team-up was Henry J., whom Dad had come to know on a road job near Redding in 1921.

Henry J. Kaiser was born in Sprout Brook, New York, on May 9, 1882. The hard-working family was of modest means. The boy left school at thirteen to run errands for a store at $1.50 a week, and worked as a photographer at nights. He became expert at "see the birdie," saved his pay, and bought out his employer, all in the American tradition. He showed early capacity for spreading out around the map—camera-snapping tourists in Florida in the winter and vacationists in Lake Placid, New York, in the summer. A subject for his lens at Lake Placid was a tall, lively young lady from Boston.

Love's arrows pierced the black cloth. The girl's father forbade marriage unless Henry could build her a home and earn $125 a month. So Henry crossed the continent to Spokane, Washington, and went to work—first as a salesman in a hardware store, then for a sand-and-gravel plant, which he was soon running. Whatever else the future held for him, and it was plenty, he never was to get away from those basic building ingredients. He was to become one of the colossal sellers, haulers, mixers, and emplacers of sand and gravel and its accompanying materials—cement and steel. In one year Henry fulfilled the conditions laid down for his marriage, returned to Boston, announced "I'm ready," and, in 1907, wed Bess Fosburgh.

He learned paving with a company which was laying down Spokane's streets. In 1913 he went into the game for himself with some secondhand wheelbarrows, some concrete mixers, and a couple of teams. The horse traffic of Nanaimo, Victoria, and Vancouver was partially lifted out of the mud by his pavements. When a gas tax began to finance highways over the northwestern United States, he moved to Everett, Washington, and then to Seattle. While on a paving job at Mount Vernon, Washington, he devised something new—rubber tires for wheelbarrows. His men doubled their handle and saved their muscles, and manual labor woke to the fact that here was one of the finest inventions since payday.

Henry's first meeting with Dad Bechtel came about when Dad went up to the Red Bluff-Redding job to sell Henry on joining the Contractors' Association of Northern California. Henry thought he wouldn't join, and Dad needled him. "Okay, not a good sport, eh?" Henry replied, "I'll join." That began a friendship lasting as long as W. A. Bechtel lived. Henry went on in Dad's footsteps to become president of the Northern California chapter of the National Associated General Contractors of America.

In 1921 a $500,000 contract was to be let for a 30-mile Red Bluff-Redding highway in extreme northern California. For this, Kaiser and Bechtel opened that rock plant at Oroville. It was one stage of the grand-right-and-left between Kaiser, Bechtel, and other western contractors, the swing-your-partners pattern which was to take them whirling into many corners of the globe, by no means ending with the big dam on the Colorado.

For the next ten years Henry Kaiser built highways and drove over highways, with his wife beside him and two sons bouncing on the back seat. He also did levee work on the Mississippi.

A handsome subcontract came his way in the middle twenties: 200 miles of concrete roadway and bridges in Cuba. Kaiser had sensed the oncoming mechanical age. He moved in with concrete mixers of unusual size, big power shovels, and deisel tractors, and finished three years ahead of contract schedule. He'd opened up about thirty rock quarries and sandpits, handy to the job, cutting down transportation time.

Henry J. had just about mopped up the Cuban undertaking when Steve Bechtel, in 1928, approached him with the suggestion of putting some of his energy to work, along with Steve's, on the midwestern big-inch Continental Gas pipeline. The sand and gravel man went along.

But while lying awake nights in Cuba, trying to figure out what his organization could handle next, Kaiser hadn't been thinking pipelines. He had been thinking Black Canyon. He'd said to A. B. Ordway, his general superintendent, "Ord, the only way to handle that job is to pool the manpower of a group of western contractors." That's what H. W. Morrison of Boise,

Idaho, had been thinking, too. When Morrison learned that Kaiser was also putting a combination together, he wasted no time fighting the adversary—he straightway went to Kaiser and found Henry already convinced that the job was big enough for Morrison-Knudsen, Utah, and the Bechtel and Kaiser groups, too.

By 1929 the Wattises had also been considering the proposed big dam on the Colorado and wondering if they couldn't swing that contract for themselves. Guy Stevick, who later became a director of the Six Companies, representing the surety companies that jointly put up bond, recalls what happened next:

One day in 1929, Mr. Harry Morrison of the contracting firm of Morrison-Knudsen Company called at our company office at San Francisco and said that two brothers, W. H. and E. O. Wattis, representing a corporation called Utah Construction Company, had invited him to join with them in a bid on the Boulder Dam contract, and that it might run fifty million dollars or more. They desired to consult with my company about furnishing a bond guaranteeing the performance of the contract. I went with Mr. Morrison to the office of the Utah Construction Company in the Phelan Building, a very meagerly furnished office. . . . I explained to them that all surety companies acting together would not furnish the bond unless the contractors showed at least five million dollars cash available for the work. Mr. E. O. Wattis showed some disappointment but asked for suggestions from those present as to who might be asked to join them. They had already discussed the Bechtel Co. and Henry Kaiser; I suggested that our experience with MacDonald & Kahn had been very favorable. Mr. Charles Swigert and Mr. Philip Hart, representing the

Pacific Bridge Company, and Charles Shea were suggested and discussed.

Soon after, old W. H. Wattis, the dying president of Utah Construction, gave the approval that placed Utah Construction Company in the combination and made organization of the Six Companies possible.

Six Companies, Inc., as the group styled itself, was put together in February 1931, just two weeks before the bids were due. Kaiser and Bechtel, with an assist from the Warren Brothers of Cambridge, Massachusetts, came in for a million and a half. Morrison-Knudsen, with some scratching about, dug up a half million. So did the pugnacious Charlie Shea, and he brought in Pacific Bridge Company of Portland for a like sum. With Utah Construction and MacDonald & Kahn each putting up a million, there was the capital required to attract the bondsmen. As matters turned out, the whole five million was actually not needed for working capital, for the winning bid shrewdly specified an unusually high payment for the early work of excavating, balanced off by a very low reward for the later work of concrete pouring; so by the time big cash was needed, it was coming in from Uncle Sam in fistfuls.

March 4, 1931, was the day for opening the bids in Jack Savage's office at Denver. The bidders at the showdown were three. Six Companies was the lowest—its $48,890,996 was five million under an Atlantic coast syndicate and ten million under a team from the Middle West.

Six Companies, Inc., hadn't shaved it as fine as a winner likes—but the group had the contract.

What the partners didn't foresee was that the job, involving unprecedented engineering and construction ingenuity, would usher in a whole new age of earth changing.

To the waiting people in Tar Town came the news of the contract letting. "It's gone through! It's going to happen!" cried Tooe Erlander.

"Yobs for everybody!" cheered Olof.

"I'll be a water boy," said Peter.

Molly Erlander asserted, "They'll want girls, too. I'll learn how to run a typewriter."

In a shack a mile away Art Lloyd, who hadn't met Olof Erlander yet although the wives were friends, said to his Shana: "There'll be tunnels. I'm a miner. It will feel good to get underground again."

Said Llewellyn Lloyd, who was eighteen and looked older, "I'm going to stay out in the sun and drive a truck."

3

THE MAKING OF TWO TITANS

MOLLY ERLANDER, seventeen and blue-eyed, and slim and yellow-crowned as a stem of Minnesota goldenrod, learned stenography and got her job. She found it in the shanty office that the dam superintendent had erected on the dizzy verge of Black Canyon.

She came to know the two men her father had seen that wintry day in 1930—Frank Crowe and H. W. Morrison. She learned that Mr. Morrison had had a chief hand in putting the Six Companies together. When the bidding proved successful, and responsibilities were assigned among the principals, he alone had nothing to do. And that turned out to be as he wanted it, so long as he had his man, Crowe, bossing the job. If Molly had known what the word meant, she'd probably have called H.W. the catalyst of the Hoover Dam crowd —the one who'd blended those rivals, all rugged individualists, into a team of high-powered doers.

Crowe, the sharp-tongued fellow with the baggy pants and the old hat speckled with concrete, was forever standing about scratching his chin and thinking up ways to make hard things easy. Tales about him were many—how he built a timber housing over a dam excavation in Wyoming, put stoves in the structure, and poured concrete all winter long—the concrete safe from freezing; how he slung horizontal cables across the chasm of Arrowrock Dam on Boise River, and on those "Joe Magees," so named for the first man who rode them, he sent concrete carriers whizzing out from the rim of the canyon to dump and pour at a record clip. The device had made history at Arrowrock, and it was to make still more at Hoover. "Molly, I can't see why anybody would work in a city office when he can be in a place like this," Crowe would say. Face leathered and eyes wrinkled from staring up from river bottoms, Crowe was the "Old Man" to everybody who came into the shanty, and he'd been called that for a decade or two, she learned, though he was not yet fifty. He was the whip around the place that made men hop.

On the other hand, H.W.—nobody but his wife Ann called him Harry—had been white-haired since he was thirty, according to jolly Ann, and though three years younger than Crowe he seemed more truly the "Old Man." Like Crowe, he too was a bundle of intensity, but he was also a very kindly person to those around him. Knowing Crowe's dislike of interference, he kept his calls to a minimum.

Once or twice he sat down in the office to wait for the superintendent, though waiting was a hardship for him. But his eyes were busy, taking in the work below. Molly was sure he missed nothing, that the movement of every truck and wheelbarrow had a meaning for him. Yet when Crowe came, Mr. Morrison had no suggestions to offer; the responsibility here belonged to the man with the battered hat. The visit of the man from Boise had to do with another dam altogether.

Always there was another dam, canal, or tunnel. It was clear that Mr. Morrison wanted the mighty job below Molly's

window to hurry up and get finished, that his mind was busy
with a dozen more projects. This craggy-looking, self-driving
man who found it so hard to sit still, whose eyes were always
roving and fingers drumming, was destined to play an important role in erecting more than two thousand major works,
of which Hoover Dam would be but one. He was to become
the prime earth and rock mover of all time. But Molly couldn't
see the future and didn't know his past.

Harry Winford Morrison was born of Scotch-Irish parents
in DeWitt County, Illinois, in 1885. His dad ran a grist mill.
His mother died when he was four, and he bobbed about
among relatives. At fourteen he found a summer job as water
boy for a Chicago contractor and at seventeen he went to
work as timekeeper for that firm, Bates & Rogers, who were
building Minidoka dam and powerhouse on the Snake River
in Idaho. A serious, shy youngster, his formal schooling
stopped with two years in high school and a shot at business
college.

The Snake River at Minidoka is in another western straight-
walled gorge hundreds of feet deep, and the black lava region
known as Craters of the Moon—a grim waste—is only 40 miles
north. But young H.W. fell in love with the yellow and green
cliffs, black ridges, rivers that spout out from underground,
and breadth of horizon that was Idaho. When he saw what
water did for the desert he knew or sensed what he was going
to do for the rest of his life—push rock, turn rivers, make the
earth more useful.

After Minidoka dam, Morrison put in several years with
the Reclamation Service, now called the Bureau of Reclamation, as axman, chainman, rodman, foreman, draftsman, and
superintendent. He spent his nights battling correspondence

courses in engineering. A gangling, boyish-looking chap with prematurely graying hair, he was sent to Boise Diversion Dam in 1908 to see why the crews there were giving trouble. Morris Knudsen, boss of the job for the Reclamation people, and twenty-three years Morrison's senior, took a look and said to his wife, who was running the cookhouse, "Why, Ma, they've sent only a kid." The kid began to deliver the crackling sentiments that work so well with construction stiffs, and the appreciative Dane hastily revised himself. "Ma, I guess they've sent us a real man."

The two, Morrison and Morris Hans Knudsen, eventually decided to go into contracting together, and they became partners in 1912 on a capital of six teams of horses, some scrapers, picks, shovels, wheelbarrows, and a few hundred dollars. They remained in double harness for the next thirty years. H. W. Morrison and Morris Knudsen—the names slid easily into Morrison-Knudsen—set up business in Boise in one room. It served H.W. as office by day, sleeping quarters by night. Knudsen, a cautious man, stayed on with the Reclamation Service until the new firm got a good start. "Mama and I will stay on the job," he told his partner. "Then if the company doesn't make a go of it, you can come back and still have a place to eat."

The first job was a subcontract on the pumping station of an irrigation project. Morrison bought a few tents and some mess equipment, rented a cement mixer, hired some help, and placed cement in the good old-fashioned way of pushing and pulling a wheelbarrow up a narrow plank by manpower and a rope. Getting paid took litigation and Harry dropped that one—his lawyer was a day late in filing a lien. It cost Morrison $1,200, but out of it he got the lawyer who'd cost him the decision—Karl Paine, who's been chief counsel for the

Morrison-Knudsen Company ever since. Morrison also gleaned a motto: "Never depend on litigation to make profit out of a contract."

Boise is the Far West in little. Morrison and Knudsen picked up contracts for logging roads, irrigation ditches, railroad and highway work. They were low bidders on Three Mile Falls Dam near Hermiston, Oregon, taking it away from Bates & Rogers, who exclaimed of their former water boy, "That damned kid!" It was a concrete multiple-arch dam 50 feet high, 1,200 feet long, for water diversion on Umatilla River. The damned kid and his partner made $14,000 and discovered that building dams could be exhilarating business.

In 1914 Harry took note of Anna Daly, a dark-eyed Boise girl born in one Idaho gold town and reared in another, where her dad ran the Last Chance mine; she was a secretary in the state insurance department. Shy but determined, Harry carried on a remote skirmish of the heart, like an Indian hurling his arrows from behind a tree. Stalking Anna, but scared to death of her, he sent messages by her sister every day, hinting at what she was missing in not becoming acquainted with him. The maid ranged from puzzled to indignant to curious. Finally they met, both ready to cut and run. The tall young fellow could twang the guitar and sing a hillbilly ditty, but what scared Anna was the intensity behind those thick brows. But within a month she found herself wondering if perhaps the life of the wife of a construction man wouldn't be romantic and interesting. They were married soon after, and it was a marriage that was to last like one of Harry's dams. For keeps.

They moved into a field camp near Payson, Utah—bleak, hot, windswept. Proud of the work he was doing, Harry took his young wife out over the job in the buckboard. He whoa'd

near the rock-crushing plant and went in to settle an argu-
ment between a foreman and an inspector. The sun blazed
down and passing trucks set up a smother of dust. Broiling-
hot hours passed. The bridegroom, forgetful of everything but
the work at hand, cleaned up and went to the cookhouse for
supper. Mama Knudsen, the camp cook, cried, "Harry, where
is Anna?" He hurried, then, to his dust-choked, indignant
bride. Ah, romance!

More construction camps, and business not doing well. Up
into the Idaho mountains the two Morrisons drove by buckboard to bid on a tunneling job. They won the job. (To this
day Ann goes with Harry on all his trips and, though the
sums run into large figures, the trips aren't always plush even
yet.)

The firm lost $17,000 on that tunnel. To Pocatello next for
enlarging an irrigation canal. They hitched up Frog and
Toad, their horses. They pitched tent in a blustering gale on
a lava sidehill and furnished it with egg crates for a cupboard
and giant-powder boxes for chairs. Anna made a carpet out
of gunny sacks. Blasts sent rocks through the tent and the
canal overflowed and flooded the floor. A hard freeze followed, turning the floor into a miniature skating rink. Harry
hadn't mentioned these items among the fascinations of contracting while plunking that guitar to his dark-eyed Irish girl.

Two years of effort should have brought a reward, but
failure was close. Harry worried desperately. He laid everybody off but himself. He cut his salary to $100 and Knudsen,
thanking his stars for his Reclamation job, took his name from
the payroll entirely until business should pick up. Ann (as
she was now called) served as the bookkeeper and stenogra-
pher without pay. This was the low of M-K fortunes. A brief
upturn followed. Morrison closed a subcontract for some

street paving in Boise. The principal job was Harrison Boulevard, where his home is today. He bought a secondhand gyratory rock crusher. It gave nothing but trouble. The crusher had an appetite for Babbit-metal bearings. Papa Knudsen became fed up with it and almost with contracting in general. Luckily the crusher burned to the ground. Today its site is a city park.

Frog and Toad gave place to a Model T Ford in 1916. The Morrisons were proud of that Ford, though it tried to crack the wrist of anyone who cranked it.

There was a job at Cascade, Idaho, and the company's work horses were stolen. The thieves were caught and the Morrisons left in the Model T for the trial at Boise. On the way, at Dry Buck Summit, it took heavy pushing to get over the top: such emergencies were frequent; Harry was half of the vehicle's power. At the trial the couple were surprised to hear themselves denounced as a rich, bloodsucking corporation—the company having less than $1,000 in the bank at the time, and both Morrisons working every day in the week, including Sundays, the year round. But the horse thieves were convicted.

A camp cook went on a bender and Ann and the single office employee at the time tackled the cooking. They produced an enormous kettle of oatmeal for breakfast and a mulligan for dinner; Ann had to stand on a box to stir. Sixty men stormed in and took their places. While the office hand carried in the food, Ann worked the dish-up table. In fifteen minutes all of the grub was exhausted. A new batch, oceans of it, was manufactured for the next meal. Again the human locusts swarmed in. Filling up construction workers proved to be a hopeless task. After several days the celebrating cook returned, a heavenly sight if a bleary one, and Ann fled back to her office work.

The next contract involved a 35-mile drive in the Model T in a November squall. Wind and rain forced them to stop and put on the side curtains. Harry's disposition grew more and more edgy. After slipping off the dirt road a couple of times, Ann driving and Harry pushing the Ford out of the ditch, they arrived at the jobsite. So did December, that year 1916. Snow was 3 feet deep and temperature 25 degrees below. They landed the job.

There was trouble at the bank in Boise; the partnership had lost track of the notes it owed, though they amounted to $100,000. (Today M-K borrows multimillions a year. The banks don't mind.) The slight case of overdraft dissolved with a couple of contracting successes, and in 1919 Harry hired a young timekeeper named Merton Kennedy. Today he's one of the eleven M-K vice-presidents, in charge of South American business.

The Model T was everywhere during those hard-battling years. It left Boise one day at 6 A.M. for a bidding on a highway job at Council, Idaho. Wind blew and clouds gathered. On went the Ford, entering a mountain canyon, swinging crosswise, sliding perilously near the edge of a thousand-foot drop, slithering toward the opposite side, then plopping into the ditch. After a thirty-minute struggle, with H.W. once more pushing, the brave little vehicle—M-K's total power equipment—was on its way again. It was 2 A.M. before Harry and Ann had the final figures added up for presentation next day. Harry said, "I'm going to add three thousand dollars for all that rain, snow, and frost." He did, and they lost the job by $2,500.

So went the days, while the H. W. Morrison character was

setting like well-poured cement. Relentless energy and inexhaustible drive. An occasional twanging on that guitar and a bit of hillbilly singing, but on the whole there was little time for fun. The highest joy was the winning of a bid; the deepest satisfaction, the knowledge of a job done well and profitably. H.W. didn't know it and Ann didn't know it—or did she?—but the number one earth mover was emerging out of these jobs on corduroy logging roads and irrigation works. The time would come when his shovels would clank not only along Snake and Clearwater but along Indus, Orinoco, and Euphrates; when he'd be saluted with wave of hat or hand not only by homesteaders in the Bitterroots but by herdsmen in the Hindu Kush and the Atlases.

In 1921 M-K acquired its first power shovel, a Marion dragline, though Papa Knudsen was hostile to such thundering gadgets and still more hostile to its cost. A $25,876 investment was soul-shaking. But a sizable drainage job in Boise Valley was in sight. The firm took the plunge and ordered the coal-burning monster with its 40-foot boom and 1½-yard bucket. The new dragline turned the tide in M-K's affairs, enabling them to undertake genuinely big things.

In 1923 the concern was incorporated and its gross volume that year passed a million dollars. The Model T, which had supplanted the buckboard, was supplanted in turn by a Cadillac. But it was a work-horse Cad. Harry lugged dynamite about on the back seat, while Ann prayed every time they hit a chuckhole, of which the Idaho roads had many.

Utah Construction Company began to feel the pressure of this hard-working contractor who was forever bobbing up in pursuit of business.

On the Boise Diversion Dam job, years before, Morrison had become acquainted with Francis T. Crowe. When Mor-

rison-Knudsen and Utah Construction jointly picked off
Guernsey Dam, Frank Crowe was named boss of the job.
After Guernsey the combined outfits built Deadwood Dam in
Idaho. There, Crowe and M-K tried something that really
dumfounded Papa Knudsen—bulldozers, diesel trucks, and
gas-powered shovels. Morrison had become convinced that
big work required big tools. Whenever he'd bought big, capable tools he'd finished up fast and made money. But these
monsters! "How are you going to get 'em up over mountains?"
worried Morris Knudsen. H.W. took them up over the steepest
and worst logging roads he could find and proved he could
get them anywhere, even over Idaho mountain passes 7,000
feet above the sea.

By the mid-twenties, M-K was a sizable organization. Morrison decided to call a three-day roundup of personnel. It was
a great get-together. M-K men and their wives poured into
Boise. The gathering ended with a banquet and dance for
eighty-five at the Eagles Hall. Four wives, including Ann and
Mrs. Knudsen, baked the cakes—it helped to cut the overhead.

Harry branched out. With friends he organized Southern
Idaho Oil Company to distribute petroleum products in that
locality, and his wife took fifty shares, closing out her savings
account to do it. Over the years the stockholders received a
series of stock dividends, but no cash. Ann began to wonder
about her $5,000. She thought of a lot of things she might
have spent it on, including a whole row of pretty hats. Then
Shell bought out Southern Idaho, paying four to one. The
news came on Ann's birthday. Harry phoned, "Dear, I have
a wonderful present for you—a check for $44,800. Meet me
for lunch at the Hotel Boise." Her head in the clouds, visualiz-
ing the wild spending spree that was to be hers at last, she
met him. After luncheon Harry said, "Hon, that's too much

money to keep in a checking account. M-K will be glad to borrow it from you at eight per cent." She fell for it, too startled to argue. Her spending spree again postponed, she walked out with a small piece of white paper in her hand which read, "I, Morrison-Knudsen Company, promise to pay to Anna D. Morrison. . . ."

Years later she received magnificent returns on her investment, the $5,000 having grown to six figures. "But somehow," she recalls wistfully, "the edge had been removed from the long-ago thrill of that imaginary spending spree."

The growing organization built a head office on the outskirts of Boise. It was a single-story brick building, designed to be readily convertible into residence property if the construction business foundered: Morris Knudsen's caution again. But the brick structure never had to become a dwelling. It is still M-K main headquarters, while M-K now has sub-offices in cities around the globe.

H.W. continued lashing along. A young bride and groom, the groom a relative of Ann's, were unlucky enough to be caught up in his tailwind. Uncle Harry and Aunty Ann invited the newlyweds to come along for their honeymoon on a Morrison business trip from Boise to Zion National Park. The quartet left Boise at 4:30 P.M. just after the wedding, and arrived at Twin Falls four hours later after a hot ride over rough roads. Reservations had been overlooked and there was a convention in town, hotels full to the eaves. Two rooms were finally located—saggy springs, shaky chair, small wall mirror, and bowl and pitcher. "Get your water from the tap at the end of the hall," said the bellhop. The bridal couple were dismayed to hear Uncle Harry put in a rising call for 5 A.M. Breakfast was in a Chinese restaurant, and all were off at six-thirty. The drive to Salt Lake City was through August dust. The call again was for 5 A.M. Harry picked up a fellow contractor and took him on the honeymoon, too. At Zion, for two nights and a day, the newlyweds were left in peace while Harry inspected a highway tunnel site. Next call, 4:40 A.M. After more days of early rising, speed, and dust, the party was back in Boise. Morrison was not the low bidder on the Zion tunnel and expressed great disappointment over the journey. What the young marrieds thought about it is lost to history.

Karl Paine, the M-K lawyer, decided to resist the famous H.W. pressure. He started with the boss from Boise one morning at daybreak to motor to San Francisco. They checked in at a hotel at Bend, Oregon, with a rising call for 5 A.M. At five-thirty Harry was in the lobby, packed and ready to be off. No Karl. Six, and six-thirty. Still no attorney. The hotel clerk rang Paine's room. But an irate stranger answered and threatened bodily injury if the phone rang again. Paine came down in good time, after an excellent night's sleep, having managed to trade rooms with a later arrival.

While being driven to a proposed job for the Union Pacific near Cheyenne, H.W. ran into a rainstorm that put a foot of swirling water over the road. He got out and walked ahead for several miles so the driver could follow the roadbed. Then water got into the motor and H.W. and a passenger had to push until it ran again. They got back into the car soaked to the waist. Always a light traveler and now caught without an extra suit, Morrison made it to the hotel in Cheyenne at midnight and sent for the presser. The suit was promised for an appropriately early hour. Harry was up at six-fifteen. No suit. At six fifty-five a group of engineers phoned from the lobby that they were ready and waiting. At seven-thirty pants and coat still had not come. The engineers phoned again.

Harry refused to explain the delay. As nothing less than the crumbling of a Morrison-Knudsen dam could have been more unlikely than a tardy H.W., speculation ran high. At seven-forty there was a valet's knock at Morrison's door, but the suit that was handed in wasn't his. The whoop of wrath which thereupon broke loose in Cheyenne had not been heard since Red Cloud's Sioux passed that way. Harry's suit, still wet and unpressed, was hurriedly located and restored to him. He put it on, and obstinately wore it for the next two days in its sorry state, finally heading homeward by rail. A washout on the line held the train up and Morrison, this time dressed exactly right for a flood, waded happily in the waist-deep deluge, the only passenger who didn't care.

In 1930, M-K was really feeling its muscles, for Boulder Dam was in the offing, and if Morrison's syndicate had the winning bid—— To San Francisco they went, a town Ann well remembered from her visit in 1922 when she had written in her diary: "Millions of twinkling lights; homes nestling in and around the hills; the downtown district . . . a veritable fairy-land; a real thrill." They'd resolved, if and when they ever made their stake, to return on a gay holiday, including that postponed shopping spree. But no holiday was yet in sight, though Harry Winford Morrison was about to make the long leap that could carry him to the status of tycoon, halfway to titan. They checked in at the Stewart Hotel and found Frank Crowe waiting. H.W. had a typewriter sent up to their room; then he, Frank, and Karl Paine, the lawyer, went into confer-ence. For the next four days Ann was kept busy typing what was to be the organizational plan for Boulder Dam. The days of hardheaded figuring began at 8 A.M. and ended at mid-night. The quartet were lucky to find time for meals.

A few weeks later the Six Companies won the big dam.

On the way home from San Francisco, via a Sierra rail-road job, Morrison became seriously ill. Ann was frightened and wanted to turn back, but her husband insisted on going on. When they reached Bieber Camp, one of M-K's jobsites, he was in the throes of a gall bladder attack. The local doctor wanted to operate without benefit of hospital. Ann balked ab-solutely. After a night of excruciating pain Harry, worn and weary, insisted upon getting up at seven-fifteen. He had come to see the work on that railroad project and he was going to do so.

They took off in a pickup truck over a rough road. Every rut they fell into was agony for the sick man, but on they went. Morrison inspected the railroad grade and the tunnel. Then they turned back for San Francisco and medical relief. Harry would have Ann stop the car and he would get out and sit for a few minutes on the running board, head in hands, and then they would go on. Inevitably, they had a flat tire. It was too heavy for Ann to handle, so Harry's big work-hands had to lift the tire off and put the spare on. It almost finished him. Alternately stretching out on the back seat, stopping the car and sitting on the running board, and climbing back to stretch on the rear seat again—unable to eat, traveling for two days, and changing yet another flat—the sick man reached the seaport city, where he was operated on. Four days of touch and go followed, then the doctor said, "Harry is going to make it." A month later he was in a wheel chair, recovering.

Mr. and Mrs. Knudsen were at the Boise depot to meet the returning pair. It was a joyful homecoming. Harry's bed was waiting for him, but he wanted to get back to work. At H.W.'s insistence, Papa Knudsen took him to the office for a couple of hours. The next day Ann succeeded in keeping him home. He wore himself out pacing the floor. On the following day she gave up, letting Harry go to the office at 8 A.M. At that, it was a half hour late for the man who had just come home with the most outstanding construction contract ever awarded, up to that time, to private industry.

Francis Trenholm Crowe, who superintended the construction of Hoover Dam, was born in Trenholmville, Quebec. After graduation from the University of Maine in 1905 as a civil engineer, he started in as a junior engineer with the U. S. Bureau of Reclamation, and joined Morrison-Knudsen in 1925. He'd previously built Jackson Lake Dam and Arrowrock. With M-K he built, within five years, four more good-sized dams, in Wyoming and the Northwest.

Although he introduced big mechanical equipment to dam building, he was in his heart a horse lover. This was a great bond between him and Morris Knudsen. As a general supervisor, Crowe knew the names of all Knudsen's horses and that made him, in the Dane's opinion, the greatest engineer who ever lived.

Frank Crowe's urgent desire to build Boulder had helped agitate H. W. Morrison to sell the idea to W. H. Wattis, and to enlist the other firms that ultimately comprised Six Companies. Crowe's erect six-foot-four figure and sharp tongue had dominated every job he'd bossed. His favorite word for a man in disfavor was "damn scissorbill!" Since Crowe's era new titles have come along, such as General Superintendent and Project Manager, but Crowe, the man who built the dam in Black Canyon that was first called Boulder, then Hoover, was known simply as Superintendent.

Frank Crowe has long been gone, in this year 1957, leaving towering Shasta Dam as well as Hoover and many another as monuments. Morris Knudsen passed away a few years after Hoover Dam was completed, while the thundering era of big-dam construction introduced by Hoover was in full swing. Papa Knudsen did not feel quite at home with the roaring machines of this new era. Horses he understood, but horse-power by the hundreds under the hood of a single piece of equipment was an awesome thing. He perhaps didn't feel too much at home with his fancy title, Chairman of the Board, either. But he had been a tower of strength.

But H. W. Morrison still is turning the world's rivers and moving its mountains. On almost any day of the year a plane is likely to touch down at Boise and out of it step a short, curly-haired woman whom everybody knows by her first name. With her is the tall, square-jawed, silvery-haired figure under a broad western hat. Ann and H.W. are back from another globe-girdling inspection trip. H.W., who used to look old for his years when Hoover Dam was going up—it was that prematurely snowy thatch that did it—now has caught up with his silvery poll and seems younger than he is. If Ann has her way, she and H.W. will go home to their comfortable one-story dwelling on Harrison Boulevard—a house they see only a few weeks out of the year.

But she doesn't have her way. H.W. goes straight to the office. At seventy-two he still bursts into a room instead of walking into it. He checks with his estimators, sees how new bids are shaping, hears what new enormities of diesel-driven equipment are wanted by his vice-presidents, and drops into the room which he calls his own, where he has a flat desk and a conference table arranged in a T. He falls to work, and he always works in vest and shirtsleeves. He rocks incessantly while at his desk cogitating the problems of a project; he still drums with his fingers while he is figuring. To those who come in, he talks fast in a low voice, difficult to hear. If the matter turns into a conference, he sits with his resident vice-presidents, J. B. Bonny, Murray E. Burns, Lyman D. Wilbur, and Carroll F. Zapp, crowding in on him—or his treasurer, E. W. Glass; his vice-president and assistant general manager, James D. McClary; his chief engineer, J. P. Frein; his comptroller, Truman Joiner; his magazine editor, Paul Nations; or his overseas district manager, L. M. Greenleaf—clasping and unclasping his hands nervously or scratching a shinbone. His nervous energy communicates itself to some of his executives until they begin crossing and uncrossing legs and scratching shinbones, too. He is in and out of the office while conversations are going on. If he has been caught by an interviewer for the newspaper, he ducks out frequently just to escape the feeling of being in the limelight. He insists he is of no particular importance as an individual, that the work his firm is doing is being done by a team.

Photographs of old cronies and past jobs line all the walls of his office but one. That wall, directly opposite his chair, is covered with a single map. Steve Bechtel, who has a liking for large maps, gave this one to H.W., and it is the only one he has in his working quarters. On a given day there are pushed into it, in some twenty-two countries and seventeen states, ninety-nine red-, white-, or yellow-headed pins. When Morrison swings his gaze toward that wall, he sees behind each pin a dam or canal or powerhouse or tunnel or highway, or a port, an airbase, a bridge, or perhaps a factory that a big subsidiary back in Ohio, the H. K. Ferguson Company, is erecting. The red pins indicate enterprises in foreign countries; the whites are domestic jobs; the yellows are joint ventures.

In his day Harry Winford Morrison, the small-town fellow
who still thinks that Boise is the finest city on earth, has built
more than $3 billion worth of structures to make the earth
yield more or to make the free world safer.

He comes back from trips with countless scraps of paper
from which he dictates letters to nearly everybody he has
seen. He comes down to his office every day, including Sun-
days, but doesn't insist that his secretary, Mrs. Petra
Asumendi, come down on the Sabbath. "He respects my Sun-
days," says pretty Petra.

Morrison is completely democratic, and at office he will go
over to the yard across the street and greet most of his workmen by name. At one time he prided himself on knowing the
name of everybody in the organization. Nowadays Ann keeps
track of people better than he does. Her memory is as fabulous
as her good nature and her faculty for making herself at home
in any setting.

The Morrisons' charities come in for attention during his
brief stays at home. But he keeps them well hidden. Their
contributions have helped to keep Boise's churches outnum-
bering its barrooms.

One of Morrison's joint-venture partners is Lou Perini of
Boston, owner of the Milwaukee Braves. When the Boise base-
ball team was having hard sledding, Morrison persuaded
Perini to use Boise as a training farm for the big-league team.
Baseball is one of the few frivolous things which stir H.W.
like the sight of a power shovel biting out yards of earth.
Football is another—the only sport he bets on. His limit is
$5.00.

Morrison doesn't like to talk about the jobs he has lost
money on. When anybody asks about them, he says, "It's history now." M-K dropped a million or so on the Broadway

Tunnel in San Francisco in 1952. Glacier Park highway cost the company heavily, largely because the surplus rock couldn't be dumped at any nearby place—might mar the scenery, said the "beauty doctors," as Morrison calls the park naturalists. He's proud of the fact that M-K has never backed out of a jinx job, but has gone ahead and finished whatever it undertook regardless of loss.

Morrison's idea is that money, like machinery, should be kept humming day in, day out. He turns his over several times a year. He is not much tempted by the lures that attract some of his former Six Companies partners, who have invested in permanent factories or pipelines or other facilities. He prefers to build for others, and move on. He wants to make all of his key people wealthy, but he doesn't want them to quit and enjoy their wealth. Harry and Ann Morrison have no social pretensions. They entertain only for their family, their close friends, and the people who work with them.

H.W. never takes vacations, probably because he finds his work more fun than any other occupation could possibly be. For relaxation he reads construction magazines. Before going to sleep he swings over to mystery stories. For music he turns on a phonograph that can play 300 records. But he'd rather be up and doing, and can't wait for morning to arrive.

All over the world Morrison's men are tackling problems that are seldom twice the same, and finding solutions never written in the book. In China, Red gunfire chased out M-K survey crews getting ready to build a Yangtse dam and a Yellow River railroad bridge. (M-K expects to go back there someday, though, and build them.) In Mexico, where Mocuzari Dam was rising on Mayo River, the stream was down to a trickle of 30 cubic feet a second one day; 48 hours later it was raging at 18,000 feet a second, and men and equipment were making for the hills. But still they found a way to get the big dam built.

Morrison men may be up along the Arctic Circle, installing roads and radar stations for the Dewline—Distant Early Warning—where the job is known as Operation Ice Cube. Or down in Brazil, making a river go uphill—boosting the Paraíba, 60 miles from Rio de Janeiro, to a reservoir 142 feet above the start of its climb. They are today in the compound of Kandahar, tomorrow in an oasis in Nejd; yesterday in a trailer camp beside the Yukon, tomorrow driving an irrigation waterway through swamp and dust in southeastern Australia, or tunneling under 10,000-foot mountains in New Zealand. In some administrative offices there are two suitcases always packed and ready, one for the arctic, one for the tropics. Off and away, on an hour's notice, Morrison's men go to change some portion of the face of the earth.

Good construction executives are an independent lot. Morrison loves such fellows and they love to turn in their licks for him. One of his lieutenants, the late Woody Williams, said of him, "You'll do more than you can do, because H.W. thinks you can do it." If a worker in any classification doesn't make good, H.W. is inclined to take the blame on himself, figuring that the fellow might have made the grade under a different supervisor. The man gets at least three chances before he's classed as a failure. Even then, when he's gone, Morrison prefers to remember what was good about him.

The boys in Boise tell with delight of one project manager who slid into a difficult job over on the east side of the Rockies, whose specialty wasn't fast work but fast talking. This genius had a flair for writing elaborate reports, and every day he sent in a detailed log telling precisely what each piece of equipment had accomplished. The logs were masterpieces, tremendously admired at headquarters. Came the fall of the year, and somebody in Boise fell to wondering whether the men and equipment would be taken out of the mountains in time or be locked in by snow. This doubting Thomas, a considerable executive in the M-K organization, went for a look-see. The project manager wasn't around. All those wonderful reports had been coming from a house of joy in Laramie. The executive closed down the high mountain work, brought the men and machines out—and still the daily accounts from the absentee manager kept arriving in Boise. Morrison fired the scamp, but to this day he shakes his head and says wistfully, "If I only had more men who could write reports the way that fellow could!"

If it isn't H.W.'s plane that landed this morning, it's apt to be that of Vice-president and General Manager Jack Bonny or one of ten other M-K vice-presidents. To keep these executives domestically on the wing requires a fleet of company-owned planes, complete with maintenance staff and shops. Even so, all overseas and most domestic travel is done on commercial airlines.

There are M-K subsidiaries in Colombia, Peru, Mexico, Guatemala, Australia, New Zealand, Great Britain, Canada, Afghanistan, Pakistan, and other lands. Holding this global chain together is another subsidiary, Morrison-Knudsen International, Inc., headquarters San Francisco.

In his seldom-visited office, H. W. Morrison takes his eye from the world map and, by a remarkable shift of focus that is peculiarly his, considers a couple of local paving jobs. One is a $3,000 schoolyard item, which he gathers in. The other is a $336,000 Broadway Bridge over the Boise River, one block from M-K headquarters. He has lost this bridge job to Bill

Woodall, a former employee who set up his own construction business after learning the M-K way of getting things done. Morrison scolds his estimators for letting that one get away, but secretly he is proud of an Em-Kayan who made good on his own and who has learned how to give his old employer a licking. For there is one thing that H. W. Morrison likes better than moving earth. That is seeing people develop. "If I've made any great success, it's in the selection of men and in uncovering initiative and ability to take responsibility" is the way he puts it. "My mistakes have been in taking jobs we shouldn't have taken. I find it hard to turn a job down." But he adds cheerfully, "M-K could lose ten million and stand it, though it would be a jolt."

Although he's away most of the time, he's usually home for Christmas, and he and Ann throw a party. It's largely for the couple of hundred old "associates." A crew puts up a circus tent on the back lawn and stuffs it with heaters. Behind the piano in the living room of the white frame dwelling with the red shutters is the old guitar which helped H.W. to win his bride four decades ago. Until recent years he would fetch this instrument, twang the strings, and sing in a cracked voice to his guests, but especially to Ann, "Let Me Call You Sweetheart" or another old favorite, "Idaho." Nowadays he confines his singing to group efforts around the piano, and the guitar stays in hiding.

Next evening there's a dinner dance, with band, for a thousand more Em-Kayans in a large hall, and soon after, with Ann beside him, H. W. Morrison is winging through the skies again. They are on their way to move more mountains, turn more rivers, of which the globe fortunately has quite a lot.

But for the moment we are back in 1931, and Hoover Dam

isn't history yet, it has only started. Frank Crowe is very much alive, the whole "spree" of great dams is still ahead, and from her window in the shanty on the rim of the Colorado River, Molly Erlander watches the work of preparing the site for the Hoover. A truck passes the door, makes a hairpin turn, and appears again. It is driven by young Llewellyn Lloyd, who is whip-strong and very good-looking; he can sing like a thrush—or a Welshman—and send his six-ton carrier around any cliffside curve that has room for its wheels. Though when he dips below Molly's window, she has to turn away. It's that kind of road.

4

MEN GREW TALLER, AT HOOVER

IN THE SHACKS of Tar Town, Nevada, more details of the work had been learned. There were to be four diversion tunnels, each 56 feet in diameter and extending around the site of the dam for 4,000 feet. Tunnels of that size were something new, and men whistled when they heard about them. How many years would it take to move that rock? Suppose the cofferdam failed when the river was in flood—what of the men in those tunnels? But before the bores could be started, even before access roads could be carved down the cliffs, the high canyon walls themselves had to be cleaned off. A pebble, falling hundreds of feet, could strike a man down with cannon force; and some of the loose chunks weren't pebbles, they were big as houses.

"They'll have to let men out over the edge on ropes," Art Lloyd said to Shana. "Some with drills and dynamite. And some with brooms." He gave thought to what it would mean, swinging hundreds of feet above the gorge's bottom, hanging against those cliffs like a window-washer. But this would be work he could lay his hand to immediately, while the tunneling was delayed. "I guess those guys will get good pay." He

looked at Shana fondly. Her clothes were shabby and thin. ·
The pay would buy her a new coat, new shoes, as well as a
lot of much-needed gear for Janie. . . .

"You stay on the level ground, or under it," Shana ordered
her miner husband.

Meanwhile Molly Erlander, typing and filing papers in the
eagle's nest of an office, had come to know a good bit about
the heads of the Six Companies, each of whom still wanted to
tell saturnine Frank Crowe how to build his dam. She'd heard
the directors argue and she'd heard them quarrel. Finally
Crowe himself had cleared them out. "You fellows stay in San
Francisco and hold your meetings," he'd said. "I'll build the
dam." The prima donnas of rock, sand, and gravel appointed
one of their number, bantam Charlie Shea, to be their go-
between, and they withdrew. As they went out, Crowe
plucked aside Felix Kahn, the slight, dark money wizard of
MacDonald & Kahn, and said, "If I am right with you, Felix,
you'll always be right with me." They shook hands on it.
Over the next few years Kahn carefully impounded Crowe's
bonuses and much of his salary, and returned it to him at the
finish, handsomely multiplied.

The impresarios divided their responsibilities. Besides Shea,
who looked after Crowe and construction, and Kahn, after
money and legal matters and the feeding and housing of thousands, Steve Bechtel, the second son of Dad, was put in charge
of administration, purchasing, and transportation. Henry
Kaiser was made committee chairman as well as given charge
of Washington contacts. The risks assumed by these private
contractors were quite unprecedented. They'd made a fixed
contract for a huge piece of performance, to be achieved
within seven years, with a $5,000-a-day penalty if they didn't
finish on time; yet the costs of labor and materials during the

years ahead were as uncertain as the future conduct of the fickle and temperamental river itself; and the engineering problems included several that had never before been faced, let alone solved. But out yonder on the opposite wall of the canyon, the outline of the soaring dam-to-be had been daubed in yellow paint. It had been done by some daring men swinging at the ends of ropes. Murmured the wife of one of Molly's employers, upon seeing that painted outline of the future dam, "Felix, you're all either courageous or crazy."

"They're both," thought Molly. "And so is my father."

Olof Erlander had been one of the painters who'd sketched that outline on the Arizona sheer wall.

During these difficult days the bride of Dan Costello, one of the young engineers, found the dust, chill, heat, and general torment of the region too much to bear. She packed her suitcase and was off for anywhere that was out. Dad Bechtel noticed her waiting for the bus and took in the situation at a glance. He approached and asked, "What's the matter?" Everything was the matter, she told him emphatically.

Then Dad, that man of wisdom and human understanding, sat down and began talking quietly to this girl who had had so much more than enough of the environs of Hoover Dam. He told her about his own hard life. That was what Construction meant. He also painted its romance, its opportunities for gifted young engineers, and its glories of achievement. Then he urged gently, "Go to Las Vegas and find a nice place to stay, but don't go any farther. Think of Danny. I'll pay your expenses."

A quarter century later, after roaming the globe with Danny and discovering the truth of what Dad had said about

Construction, she uttered this verdict with solid conviction: "Dad Bechtel was the greatest man I've ever met."

Work started. It was glorious news for the people in Tar Town. Olof Erlander had put in for one of those high-paying scaler's jobs and was daily in a rope sling known as a bosun's chair, brushing off the cliffs. Art Lloyd, whom he still hadn't met, had temporarily signed on as a powder monkey, loosening some of the dangerous material over Olof's head.

"Them kind of monkeys better have tails for that yob," muttered Olof as, secure in his sling, he watched Art and his kind go out along those ledges.

There was never any lack of things for Olof to look at and report to Tooe. A railroad, full of acute turns, was built along the canyon wall. Suspension bridges and eleven high cableways were strung across the gorge. Up-canyon, where a wide, dry wash came down to the river, a plant for handling and mixing material was rising. Soon that plant would stir up a batter that would include 5 million barrels of cement.

From his sling Olof could see the work going on at a distance, but much of the time he was quite alone with nothing about him but rock and sun. It reached 120 degrees in the shade in that spring of 1931, but out against the rock there was no shade. "Minnesota was never like this, by yiminy." The very rivets in his overalls seared and blistered. Sounds came from the bottom but they were thin and small. Men down there were nothing but moving dots. Sometimes his solitude was broken by a rattle, a roaring, and the rush of tons of rock from above. Olof kept his nerve. . . .

So it happened. A man working aloft on a ledge tripped on his cables. First warning came to Olof in a shower of little stones. They swept by him, off to one side; he shielded his head with his arm and looked up. The man was clinging up there, trying frantically for foothold. What he clung to gave way. The wall was not quite sheer at that point; his start downward was a glide. Olof, in his bosun's sling, didn't stop to think. The instinct of a painter took hold—of a man used to scaffolds and emergencies. He gauged his arc, kicked hard, and swung pendulumwise to meet the falling man. The two collided. Olof grabbed, so did Art Lloyd. The bosun's chair swung back, carrying the two of them. Olof signaled to be pulled up. It was a load on the hoisting block, and when two men arrived at the top, the winch operator looked surprised.

"Thanks," said Art, shaken.

"Ay yust come by at the right time," said Olof Erlander. And that was how Art Lloyd and Olof Erlander met.

One of the men Olof and Art came to know was Bernard Williams, a broad six-footer with gray-brown eyes and cropped hair and a stubby mustache, who for an obscure reason was called Woody. Woody was in charge of the construction of No. 4 tunnel, the one farthest over into the Arizona side of the gorge; the one Art Lloyd now went to work in. Williams was always experimenting. He didn't seem to think much of the current methods that were being used to drive those tunnels, and Art heard him say so to Frank Crowe and to Hank Lawler, the man who was in over-all charge of tunneling. Crowe and Hank Lawler didn't think much of Woody's ideas, either.

But if tunnels weren't driven through before the river came surging full tide, men would die and the whole enormous array of equipment that had been trucked and rafted into the gorge would go down the chute. The key to it all was speed with those tunnels.

"Stick around," said Woody in a low voice to Art one day. "I want you to help me tomorrow."

"It's my day off," mentioned Art mildly.

"It's mine, too," said Woody. "I'm going to use it working."

"I'll be here," Art replied.

Together they worked at Woody's invention. "Crowe and Lawler," explained Williams, "will be away all next week. Then we'll give it a try."

The thing was a set of platforms mounted at the rear of a massive truck, each tier equipped with a row of air-powered drifter drills. As soon as the bosses were off the reservation, Woody wheeled his contraption up. He called it a "jumbo." He put a man at each drill. The truck backed into the shallow tunnel. Practically standing on each other's necks, the drillers ripped into the face of the rock. In three-quarters of an hour the truck came out and the powdermen, one of whom was Art, hustled in. They, too, came out, and presently there was an underground throb, deep and momentous. Woody waved the shovels and mucking trucks in as soon as the fumes cleared. Woody's crew made hole that day. When Crowe and Lawler came back and saw how Williams had treated his mountain, they adopted jumbos as standard equipment, and soon there were as many as thirty-two men at once drilling into subterranean rock on each of all four faces, three shifts a day. Up against the rock went the jumbos. In went drills, in went powder. Out backed the jumbos, off went the powder, out came the smoke, in went the trucks and out, and the jumbos attacked again. Sometimes the triple crews made 40 feet a day. They sent out rock at the astonishing clip of 16,000 yards a three-shift stretch. On May 12, 1931, the log of the job had recorded "First shot fired for the Arizona tunnel adit." On January 3, 1932, the first tunnel was pierced. In two more months two tunnels were through, full width. And on November 13, 1932, a blast sent the river surging into tunnel No. 4 and a few hours later into No. 3.

The river was turned. It must have been surprised. Through aeons it had been going its own way. It was used to setting the pace and making the rules. Now pygmylike beings had headed it off as a cowboy shunts cattle through a gate. Each tunnel was as high as a four-story building and lined with concrete forced deeply into the seams of the mountain. Doors of steel had been placed at the tunnel portals. To bring just one of those gates to the project in disassembled parts had required forty-two railroad cars. As soon as the river was turned, excavating the bottom began. Four million tons of muck and rock had to come out, and it did come out, though the river hurled flash floods. The floods did plenty of damage. "I never saw a job where so many damn things happen!" Art Lloyd heard A. H. Ayers, chief engineer for the Six Companies, cuss aloud one day.

But the work went on, three shifts a day, seven days a week.

The poser of how to get millions of tons of lumber, steel, and concrete down into that fissure, where men stood so close that they almost trod on each other's feet, was solved by the "highlines"—cableways of a size not seen before, uniting Nevada with Arizona and blue sky with shadowy abyss. The lines crisscrossed the canyon and when the heavy hooks dipped, tons plunged and poured and rattled, but hit the mark. When they rose, daring little men often were yanked up with them, taking the short cut from bottom to top or from state to state.

The problem of how to get the huge penstocks to the site was solved by fabricating them on the spot, in a factory erected for the purpose just behind the brink. The matter of water for thousands of workers and their families was settled when a tank holding plenty of gallons was pitched atop a mountain near Tar Town's successor, Boulder City.

As engineering knots were unraveled, the men who coped with them seemed to increase in stature. Even the equipment grew. The 6- and 8-yard trucks which had started the earth hauling would soon be contemptuously referred to as "highway trucks." The 20- and 30-yard carrier and the 10-foot dozer blade were still over the horizon, though not far.

Often in the evenings Art and Shana and Olof and Tooe, who were all great friends by this time, and Molly Erlander and Llewellyn Lloyd, who were even better friends, and spriggy Winona Erlander and hundreds of others came out to the brink to view the spectacle under its myriad lights. Down, on the great hooks, concrete dropped from the sky in 8-yard buckets. Twenty-five thousand yards the first month. Then 149,000 in a month. Then 200,000. Then 10,000 yards in one twenty-four-hour day. It was almost a bucket a minute. Molly Erlander knew and kept the figures.

One evening the group watched sections of steel pipe being rolled down the roadway on dollies shepherded by tractors, and swung out into space. The sections were 30 feet in diameter and up to 3 inches of wall thickness. Up and out went the cannonlike chunks; they dangled against the sky a moment, and then dipped gently down into place, guided by signalmen stationed along the crags.

"It's a fine seven-year yob," said Olof Erlander, busting with pride at being a part of it.

"It won't last seven years at this rate," said Art. "It will be done in five."

But in much less than five years from the start, there it was, the great white wedge, its four tall intake towers standing behind it to their knees in the already-filling lake. There it was, a white statue resting on her elbows, one on Nevada, one on Arizona. On September 30, 1935, the President of the United States and various state and national dignitaries gathered at the top on a bunting-draped platform and made speeches. The dam had been originally called Boulder and changed to Hoover; now it was proclaimed again to be Boulder, just as later on it would once more become Hoover. The contractors, finishing up the details in the following year, made and divided $10,500,000, or $2.00 for each dollar they'd put up as working capital. Art and Olof's younger kids had had several good years in excellent schools that had been built in a new town 2,000 feet higher and 7 miles back from the brink. And Lew Lloyd and Molly Erlander had married and were living in one of the clean little houses. Lew was a cat skinner by this time, and a good one.

"Where are you going now?" Art inquired of Olof.

"Ay tank ay go to San Francisco and paint a new bridge. Vere you go next?"

"Up to the Columbia River. I hear these Six Companies fellows are building more dams up there. Tom Quinn and Abe Kanterwitz are going."

"Ay tank ay give rivers a rest."

5

"WE'LL BUILD ANYTHING, ANYWHERE!"

SIX COMPANIES had been set up to do one job, and now that job was ending. Unlike Hoover Dam, the alliance was not erected for the ages. Yet it was to endure beyond its expected time. Downstream from Black Canyon 155 miles was another project, Parker Dam, for impounding water for the Los Angeles aqueduct and the spinning out of more electric power. Six Companies took it and turned the responsibility over to J. F. Shea & Co. and MacDonald & Kahn; and Frank Crowe, though his neck was cricked from looking up at Hoover, moved in as top construction man for Parker, too. He borrowed Perry Yates from Bechtel to assist. Lew and Molly Lloyd left their neat home in Boulder City for the construction camp at Parker. So did some of their old neighbors.

A pair of breath-taking bridge jobs had come along, right in the middle of Hoover Dam's construction. These were the structures across the Golden Gate and across San Francisco Bay from San Francisco to Oakland—one with a span of 4,200 feet and the other an 8-mile double-decker involving twin suspensions, a tunnel, and a cantilever. The Golden Gate Bridge foundations were bid in by Pacific Bridge and Shea.

The job called for underwater work in swift tides that challenged all previous experience. One big caisson proved to be a colossal failure and had to be towed out into the deep Pacific and dropped to Davy Jones. A new one was built, big as a football stadium. This one did the work. It was lowered directly in the ship channel. The battering seas were held back; the caisson was pumped out; muck was excavated to deep-lying bedrock; forms were erected; and the south pier was poured. The north pier and its steel tower, hugging the stony north shore, had been easier to emplace. When the steel erectors took over they were half the time in cloud and the other half in sunshine, with the ocean's fogs that made skirts about the towers far beneath them.

As if in a race with the Golden Gate colossus, the five piers of the second bridge also were going into place. Including the plunge through bay-bottom mud, they were deeper, taller bridge piers than had ever been built before, and over them the Six Companies had split, coalesced into two smaller alliances, and had waged a dingdong battle.

Morrison-Knudsen, MacDonald & Kahn, Shea and tireless Pacific Bridge, with a new associate—canny Jack McEachern and his General Construction Company of Seattle—formed themselves into Transbay Construction Company and bid for the piers on both sides of Yerba Buena Island. Bechtel and Kaiser, with other associates, formed Bridge Builders, Inc., and squared off against their Hoover partners, also seeking the $11,500,000 pier contract. When the bids were opened, Transbay had the western piers, one of which was a massive center anchorage, and Bridge Builders had the eastern piers and piles, together with the painting of the entire structure from shore to shore.

Rivalry between the pier builders east and west of Yerba

Buena Island was slam-bang. Whose half of the bridge had the tallest pier? Transbay put one down 246 feet to bedrock and claimed the world's record. But Caro Jensen, Bridge Builders' general superintendent, rechecked his depth for the first pier on his side of the island and found it to be 247 feet. Hooray for our team! Big steel caissons were built ashore, towed out, and sunk, their sharp cutting edges taking them down to the bearing surface. West of the island there were heavier tides, more trouble, and a near disaster when one of the piers began to tip. It was righted just in time by divers working with jets of compressed air under the bottom of the tremendous structure.

Atop the tall piers of the Bay Bridge, Olof Erlander plied his paint sprayer. Sometimes he looked down, but not often. It was a long way down there. He, too, felt the stir of things out here in the western country, and struggled with a new phraseology that had entered the construction business. To Tooe he said, "Ay spent twenty years learning to call a yob a job, and now they call it a goddam proyect!"

In spite of their splits and rivalries as bridge builders, the leaders who were at that moment finishing Hoover Dam continued to join forces on other undertakings. Often they sent for Frank Crowe to lend his counsel. A new pattern of joint venturing was beginning to take form. This was the "sponsorship" idea—one member taking over the direction of a job and the others coming in as more or less silent sharers who simply lent manpower and experience when requested. It replaced the unworkable "committee" idea that had so plagued Frank Crowe. The "sponsor" usually was and is the firm that lined up a job and obtained the contract. Assistance from his coventurers is not offered nor expected unless a real need develops, and this is for the sponsor to determine. Participation, win or lose, is governed by the financial stake of each venturer. Men and firms team up to do some jobs, while entering into spirited competition for others. In large jobs the joint venture permits contractors to spread the risk. It is a pattern that has since proved useful to contractors all over the nation; it was largely stimulated by war's onsweep. But war was only a dimly seen cloud when the Six Companies, with Hoover Dam still to finish, went after another pair of big dams.

Bonneville was first. This was a project of the Army Engineers. The Colorado River had been a terror and it had been tamed; but the Columbia, a much larger stream, gathers and bears down its basin a quarter to a third of all the river horsepower of North America. Its side banks are none too secure.

While some of the partners hesitated, Kaiser moved. The man with the shiny large head and the large imagination saw in Bonneville, as later at Grand Coulee, an opportunity to turn a second and a third triumph, to make a few hazardous millions, and to keep that hard-muscled organization together that had been trained to the bone in Black Canyon. He still calls Bonneville "the riskiest of all jobs." Included in the organization was his son, Edgar, twenty-five, steady-eyed and thoughtful, who had been bossing an excavation gang at Hoover.

Kaiser's ambitions with regard to Bonneville won the approval of Felix Kahn, Harry Morrison, and Utah Construction. But Henry didn't quite corral Charlie Shea, Gorrill Swigert, and Jack McEachern. The latter three bunched by themselves and bid against Kaiser and his allies, but lost. Two months after, they reversed things by taking the Bonneville powerhouse contract away from the Henry J. forces.

Henry began to make the Bonneville gravel fly. His son

Edgar and Clay Bedford, thirty, were project manager and superintendent, respectively. The big dam 40 miles east of Portland was rammed into place in four years instead of the allotted five, and the associates in their various combinations made $3 million or so out of it. The House of Kaiser was beginning to be heard from.

The second generation was taking hold. E. O. and W. H. Wattis were gone now, W.H. without ever having seen Hoover Dam and E.O. without seeing it finished. Upon the death of W. H. Wattis, Dad Bechtel had moved up from first vice-president to president of Six Companies, Inc., and his son Steve, who would later make construction history in his own right, had become first vice-president and member of the four-man executive committee. But Dad didn't live to see the Hoover Dam or the big Bay Bridge finished, either. Hank Lawler, next in command of Utah after the Wattis brothers, Charles Swigert and Philip Hart of Pacific Bridge, Allan MacDonald of MacDonald & Kahn, and Charlie Shea, the little Irishman with the fighting heart, also passed. This should have dissolved the Six Companies, but it didn't. The combination went ahead and, between '34 and '38, raised into place, to name only a handful of projects among many, Ruby Dam and Gray's Harbor jetties in Washington, a fairylike span of concrete for the Coos Bay Highway in Oregon, and tunnel work in California—some of the latter with acute results. Utah Construction, Bechtel, Morrison-Knudsen, and Kaiser teamed up on the Dotsero cutoff and the lining of the Moffatt Water Tunnel and built Taylor Park Dam, all in Colorado.

The Delaware River aqueduct tunnel became another ambition of the associates. Felix Kahn, the son of a rabbi with the training of an engineer, likes to cite that one as an example of the joint-venture scheme of things. "I went east with Les Corey and we found we had the winning bid for part of the tunnel. I called up the other fellows and asked what percentage each wanted. And that's the way agreements were handled in the Six Companies, without a scratch of a pen. The papers were executed later, and when signed they were usually not even read."

If Hoover was the Venus of dams, Grand Coulee was the Hercules. The Army Engineers and the Reclamation people had been jockeying around the Columbia basin for some time. The hatchet between the two government agencies hadn't been buried when Army carried off Bonneville. Reclamation came back with Grand Coulee, 467 miles up the Columbia. And it was really something: not as high or thick as Hoover, but three and a half times longer. It had the bulk of the three -chief Egyptian pyramids combined.

The same month, May 1934, that saw the Six Companies divided into two camps and bidding against each other for Bonneville saw the specifications for the first unit of Grand Coulee cross their desks. On this, they were a unified group again.

Some of the constructors had been out there and looked down. It was another of those straight drops into a chasm, here 600 feet deep, but this chasm was about a mile wide. And how about those unstable banks? And all that power-packed water? The government said, in effect, "Here is our proposed method for diverting the river. You bid a lump sum for doing it this way. If you want to do it by a different method, submit your plan and we will consider it."

The scope and hazards of Coulee clearly called for the full strength of the old alliance and some new associates as well.

H. W. Morrison faces the future from Grand Coulee.

What goes up must come down. Site, Grand Coulee.

An avalanche? No, just Grand Coulee.

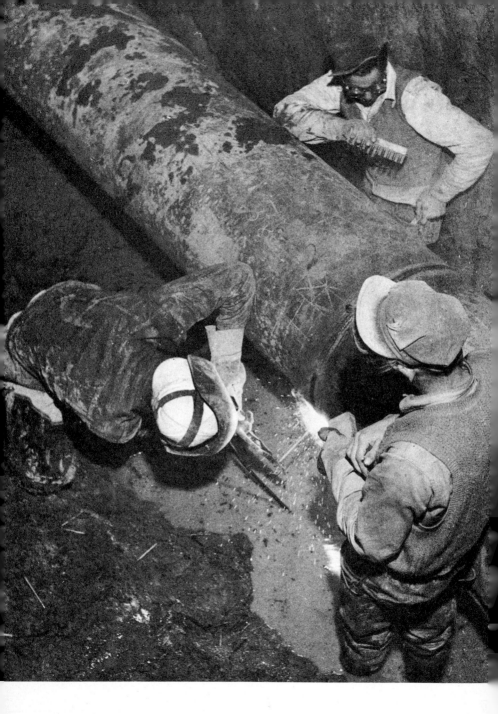

"Golden Weld" on Trans Mountain Pipeline.

Trans Mountain—where tractors played yo-yo.

Welding and lowering a section of Trans Mountain.

Steve Bechtel and his panama in Venezuela. Left, Kenneth Bechtel.
Right, George Colley, Jr.

Aden—the gas pump of the East.

At the showdown there were two bidders: Six Companies, in full force, and a syndicate composed of Silas Mason Company of New York, Walsh Construction Company of Davenport, Iowa, and Atkinson-Kier of California.

The Six Companies were very sure of themselves. Rumor had it that Mason Company was having difficulty making surety bond and that Atkinson-Kier was still undecided. For the Six Companies the job appeared to be in the bag. Henry J. invited his partners and their wives to a banquet the evening before the bidding. The associates worked on their estimates all day. Came dinnertime, they were seated at one large table. The floral decorations were handsome; the food abundant; there were cheers and applause. The party broke up at midnight. That night Tom Walsh of Iowa arrived by plane and went into a huddle with Silas Mason. What Tom Walsh brought was dough, in a large bundle.

The next day bids were opened in the office of the Reclamation Bureau. The Six Companies' principals sat smugly in the front row. When the officer read the first bid, of Mason-Walsh-Atkinson-Kier for $29,500,000, there was consternation.

The Six Companies' bid was $34 million. This group didn't wait to hear their own figure. They just got up and filed out. In an hour or two there wasn't a Six Companies' man to be found in town.

Grand Coulee was so big that $29 million covered only the excavations and foundations. MWAK did sensational work, one feat being to freeze the pestiferous slide area with brine pipes while resloping its grade. That held the bank in place. When the digging and anchoring had been done, at little or no profit to the doers, Kaiser and Mason-Walsh-Atkinson-Kier got together and agreed to pool resources, manpower, and equipment for the second slice of the work. They beat the only other bidder by a margin that made their knees wobble —over $7 million. The new combine made Kenry Kaiser its president and Kaiser nominated his able son Edgar to run the show, along with fast-rising Clay Bedford.

On March 22, 1941, Grand Coulee Dam first turned its mighty generators and was a working reality.

By that time even a Grand Coulee was only one project among many. The members of the Six Companies, jointly or individually, or sometimes with different partners, were ready to build anything—anywhere.

In the light of all that has since happened to the heavy construction industry, and the curious impact of a handful of western constructors on the scope and sweep of things all over the globe, the question arises: "Why are so many of the international construction firms headquartered on the western edge of the continent?"

The answer is several-fold. Much of the West is arid, so here the big reclamation expenditures were made. The West has always challenged man to subdue its mountains and streams and deserts. The pioneering spirit still is very much alive. There also is the long arm of coincidence, which could and did reach out and place a Wattis and a Lawler, a Mac-Donald and a Corey, a Morrison, a Knudsen, a Crowe, a Kaiser, a Shea and a Swigert, a sheaf of Bechtels, an Atkinson and a Pomeroy, and several others all on one stage. But in the astonishing development of American heavy construction on a world basis that has occurred in the last quarter century, one early influence remains paramount—the challenge, in engineering, construction, and organization, laid down by Hoover Dam. To this day, "I was at Hoover" is any construction man's proud claim to membership in the elect. And high among the achievements at Hoover was the discovery that men in the lustily combative business of big construction could nevertheless find a formula for working together. Bill Waste, executive officer of Steve Bechtel's present-day, many-ringed circus, saw the formula develop and gives this description of it:

A grass-root alliance of constructors was formed for Hoover Dam which proved the forerunner of most of the later western joint ventures. Here was a corporation made up of competitors setting out to do with their combined resources what no one of them could do alone. It was a joint venture in corporate form, geared to a single job from the outset. Probably it was the first of its kind, and certainly the first large-scale "contractors' cooperative." Furthermore, it was an open-handed, hale, hearty, and typically western relationship in every characteristic. The changing perspective of time has given it added significance as the curtain raiser on western construction's "age of giants."

The fact that in the ensuing 20 years members of this group completed private and public projects valued in the billions, and that several now are counted among the world's most powerful engineering-construction organizations, gives strong proof of the success of the joint venture.

Branching out in a score of directions, the men who had built Hoover, or some of them, were equipped for some spectacular feats when Japanese planes appeared over Oahu.

6

DRUMS OF WAR

CARL ERLANDER, Olof and Tooe's second son, heard the news. "Ma!" he cried that December Sunday, "it's on the radio!"

Olof and Tooe heard it. Their eldest boy, Peter, was out in the Pacific, working for Morrison-Knudsen on a coral dot called Wake.

"What does it mean?" Tooe asked her husband.

"It's not good. Var's never good."

Carl asserted, "Peter will take care of himself, and plenty of Japs, too. Pa, I want to get in on this!"

"Ve'll all be in," said Olof.

Between September 1939, when Hitler invaded Poland, and December 1941, when Japan blasted the Pacific fleet, America had been mobilizing her constructors. Bechtel took on the Navy's air station at Corpus Christi, Texas, and herded seven thousand builders to the task. Morrison and an associate, Ford J. Twaits, started Fort Ord and Camp Roberts in California. Other members of the Six Companies group were similarly involved. Soon the projects totaled $108 million, making Hoover Dam's budget seem peanuts. The group built copper mining plants, powder plants, airfields, shipways, and embarkation ports, and each job gave them muscle for another. Bechtel alone would soon build enough ships, a billion dollars' worth, to stretch a more or less solid bridge, if lined up, from England to France.

Vice-Admiral Ben Moreell at Washington had foreseen the need for a chain of Pacific island naval air bases and wangled an initial appropriation from Congress. Before the work was done the figures would run to half a billion, and Japanese fleets that lie rusting at the sea's bottom off Midway and many another isle are proof that Moreell's bases were useful. What turned into a race against time, with the lives of nations at stake, started modestly enough—with $63 million—and Admiral Ben invited three groups of contractors to consider it. The weather was extremely hot in Washington that day and Charley Dunn, one of Morrison-Knudsen's big-caliber engineers who sat in on the conference, remembers with delight that a commander, whose sparse hair was slicked over the top of his bald head, leaned back too far, got near the air fan, and was sucked into a vortex that all but scalped him. The first disbursement for Pacific bases went to Turner Construction and Raymond Concrete Pile of New York and Walter Dillingham's Hawaiian Dredging Company of Honolulu. But construction increased so swiftly that Bechtel, Morrison, Utah, and another far westerner, Jack Pomeroy, were soon drawn into it, together with the Byrne Organization of Dallas, which took on a big naval hospital for Oahu. The idea was to build a ring of air power from Hawaii down through Palmyra, Johnston, and out through Midway, Wake, Guam, and the Philippines, with its home base at Alameda on San Francisco Bay.

The contract drawn up by Ben Moreell was on a cost-plus-fixed-fee basis, a protection for the public treasury. No more cost-plus-percentage, which had proved such an encourager of extravagance in World War I.

So the mobilized construction men of the country bull-dozed islands, hollowed out mountains, chewed up coral, and spread seaplane landings and naval facilities for 4,700 miles outward from the continental mainland.

Pearl Harbor adjoins Honolulu on the west, and it is a harbor with several fingers. Bulldozers moved into the nearby cane and pineapples.

On the other side of Oahu Island, shining Kaneohe Bay rippled under sea winds. It, too, was in for a transformation.

Eight hundred miles below the equator, a barren atoll slumbered. It had belonged strictly to the winds; but now Johnston Island was to become a stopover for navy planes, and half a hundred suction dredgemen, dynamiters, and mechanics landed upon it from an American navy ship. They blasted a channel into the lagoon and built runways.

Palmyra was next. The palms were graceful and seemed to promise a Polynesian girl behind every tree. The damsels weren't there, but a work schedule was. Palmyra was still getting the pile driver and dozer treatment when Midway, 1,300 miles northwest of Honolulu, beheld another construction vanguard wade in through the surf.

Midway already had a transpacific cable station and a Pan-American landing strip. Fifteen hundred cat skinners, cement mixers, plumbers, carpenters, electricians, mudsuckers, and pile drivers soon were sharing tiny Midway.

Then Congress tripled the appropriation for Pacific island bases. The whole Hawaiian string was to be converted into a complex of radio stations, airfields, ammunition dumps, rifle ranges, and housing projects, and Wake, Samoa, Guam, and Manila brought into the scheme.

Utah Construction Company's responsibilities included remaking Samoa; Morrison-Knudsen caught Wake in the grab bag; Pomeroy's outfit drew Guam; and Bechtel took the task of setting up a naval seaplane base at Cavite on Manila Bay.

The lucky ones were the Utah workers. Tutuila Island in Samoa had everything as proclaimed by novelists from Stevenson to Maugham, including jungle and mountain scenery, bananas, papayas, and blouseless Polynesian girls in wraparound skirts. The Japs later paid a visit by air but they didn't swoop down to take over that eternal summer resort. Rain over happy Tutuila sometimes was a foot a day, but it wasn't TNT. Matters were different on Oahu, Midway, Wake, Guam, and Luzon.

Meanwhile something was happening under a mountain just behind Pearl Harbor. This was mysterious Project No. 16. The Navy had worried long about its vulnerable fuel tanks on Oahu. It decided to go underground.

Red Hill is a volcanic ridge several thousand feet long. In 1940 it was covered with sugar cane and pineapple bushes. This was something new to hard-rock miners used to the limestones and granites and basalts of the Rockies and the Cascades. The boys in the hard hats came with a will; they thought life was going to be one long hula to the strains of a ukulele.

At one time three thousand human moles were at work in that labyrinth. Some of these were high-scalers who had worked on the canyon walls at Hoover Dam—here they were, roped to the job again, but inside the mountain, not outside. Some were steel erectors who had helped fit the pieces of the

San Francisco Bay bridges into place. No more ocean wind
and fog in this stifling, steaming hell. They hit an underground river and had to control it. They sweated in temperatures that were seemingly only a little below those which had
created the fiery hill. Men were hurt and sixteen were killed.
Two of the latter were drowned from a capsized boat inside
the mountain while inspecting a cistern. But the $42 million
worth of vaults, pipes, valves, pumps, and portal doors were
put in place. The vertical shafts from topside were plugged
with concrete. The oil came over from the mainland by way
of a bridge of tankers, and nothing the Japs could do now,
short of taking Oahu itself, could ever prevent the Pacific fleet
from having fuel.

Harry Morrison also readied Midway and Wake for battle.
When the attack on Midway came, the Fleet air arm, with
the island base assisting, turned in one of the critical naval
victories of history.

Wake didn't fare as well as Midway. It was carried on the
points of Japanese bayonets, its garrison and construction
workers killed or taken away to prison camps.

When Olof and Tooe learned that their eldest son, Peter,
had disappeared on the fall of Wake, they became ship-
builders for war at Kaiser's Richmond, California, yard No. 1,
and so did Carl, Magnus, Winona, and everyone they knew.

Here, and in other yards of the nation, was being written
one of the dramas of industry. If Hoover Dam had developed
relatively unknown western contractors into tycoons, the current emergency had turned them into titans.

The innocence of inexperience helped Hoover Dam's builders to turn out the fleets that now began hitting the water. If
they'd known much about ships they'd have been frozen into

old procedures, and on such procedures the nation simply couldn't wait. So the builders of dams and bridges turned shoreside shallows into shipways, housewives and waitresses into welders, and night into day. They assembled portions of the vessels as far away as Denver and brought them to the Pacific's edge and welded them into hulls that went straight to sea. The figures are something to regard: the first ship in 1941, and a ship every 10 hours 18 minutes by 1943. Under the driving rivalry of Edgar Kaiser at Portland and Bechtel associate John McCone at Los Angeles, eighteen ships a month went flying down the ways at the north and twenty at the south. Kaiser-run yards at Richmond under Clay Bedford and the Kenneth Bechtel-run Marinship yard at Sausalito, both on San Francisco Bay, also added to the splash. Within two years the Six Companies group, plus other partners, were handling a $3-billion sheaf of orders for Liberty ships, tankers, Victory ships, tank landing ships, frigates, and troopships. If Tooe was late getting home to cook supper, or Olof home late to eat it, it was because they and a quarter-million other women and men from all walks of life were swarming over those hulls from Puget Sound to Santa Barbara Channel.

In this Six Companies' shipbuilding activity, the houses of Kaiser and Bechtel were the chief sponsors, but ships were only part of the show: separately or together, the old allies were all over the map on other war work. It included military highways, powder plants, graving docks, and the raising of sunken ships; the modification of bombers for special conditions as fast as Willow Run could turn them out; a 400-mile pipeline through arctic conditions in the Yukon, and airfields in Alaska.

Down in Sunnyvale, California, a hamlet surrounded by orchards south of San Francisco Bay, slumbered a rundown plant known as Joshua Hendy Iron Works. It was bankrupt, and a receiver was keeping it running with sixty doleful workmen.

Felix Kahn and one Charles E. Moore, who'd sold machinery to Hoover Dam, heard that the Bank of California wanted out of its investment, and badly. More than a year before Pearl Harbor they picked it up for the debt upon it, about $325,000. Charlie Moore wanted to sell the tools in the sagging sheds and make a quick $100,000 profit. If he'd known what was ahead within the next thirty months, he'd have collapsed for lack of breath. What was ahead for those wooden barns was 11,000 workers, 750 EC-2 Liberty reciprocating steam engines for America's emergency maritime fleet, steam turbines for faster ships, turbogenerators, turbine-drive reduction gears, diesel engines, and ships' line shafting and torpedo-tube mounts representing at one moment, all told, $125 million in unfilled orders.

When Moore suggested the Hendy purchase to MacDonald & Kahn, and they bought it and almost immediately acquired $10 million in navy contracts, Felix Kahn called up the lodge brothers of the Hoover Dam days and offered each a piece. And almost before they knew it, the dam builders were in the marine engine and torpedo mount business. Ugly, ponderous but reliable Liberty engines, two stories high and rowboat slow, managed for many months to keep the American and British merchant fleets from being driven from the seas, and Hendy made one-third of them; and Hendy's torpedo-tube mounts helped blast the Japs from the islands of the mid-Pacific and from Okinawa.

George S. Colley, Jr., the George who had been a playmate of the Bechtel boys when Dad Bechtel was building roads and railroads early in the century, had a view of the war from one constructor's level. As the house of Bechtel expanded, George had developed with it as one of its senior partners. In January of 1941, with no funds yet voted by Congress, the eight associated Pacific Naval Air Base contractors were asked who would take on the job of tidying up the Philippines, construction-wise, for the impending shooting. "We will," said Steve Bechtel to Chief Moreell of the Bureau of Yards and Docks. He added, "George Colley can get people to do what they don't know they're capable of." George whipped aboard a plane for Manila. He was going to be gone a long time.

Commander Jim Wilson met the quiet, square-built, heavy-browed engineer and informed him that the Navy had no blueprints for what it wanted, but it had the list—twenty-seven items, involving dredging, seaplane ramps, fuel and ammunition storage, powerhouse, living quarters, and hangars. First off was modernization of the installations at Cavite on Manila Bay. Said General MacArthur to George soon after, "I pray to God you will finish in time—but I do not think you will."

There was only one dredge around, and no steel nearer than Hong Kong. George hornswoggled the dredge from the Philippine Government, the steel from the British, and went to work. It was a race against the clock. And MacArthur was right—the clock won. Clark Field got its "Pearl Harboring" one day after Pearl did. So there in the Philippines were Colley and his workers, mounting antiaircraft guns, digging trenches, improvising air-raid shelters, and moving spare ammunition, mines, and explosives out of the Navy Yard.

One night Admiral Rockwell, on Corregidor, told Colley over the phone line that the navy ammunition dump on

South Manila Bay hadn't been blown up lest the villages go with it, and would Colley's gang kindly undertake its destruction by other means? Colley agreed to take the stuff out into the bay and sink it. "The next day was a busy one for all hands, with practically no sleep. I received a flesh wound in the hip from a bullet which, although not of a serious nature, bled a great deal and was inconvenient," George wrote in his journal.

Cavite's and Sangley Point's installations, not yet completed, were wiped out on December 10. The construction men were then taken to Mariveles, Bataan Peninsula, to build emergency airfields and tunnel the mountains for ammunition dumps.

Between San Francisco and the Philippines, Steve Bechtel and George Colley talked by phone every night. On December 28 George said, "You won't hear from me again for about a month." It was all he could say at the time; the Japs were on the line.

About four o'clock on the morning of January 1, 1942, General Jones's Army of Southern Luzon retreated around Manila toward the Bataan Peninsula; Colley's men retreated to Manila with the army rear guard, helping to blow up bridges.

There was no further work that they could do, so it appeared advisable for Colley to go to Pearl Harbor. He sensed that construction engineers would be in demand. "My thoughts were further stimulated by advice from Naval Intelligence that the Japanese were taking a poor view of my activities."

He shoved some key papers of his job into a briefcase. With his wife Marjorie, Harry Webber of his staff and wife, and a friend, Dr. Ashton Laidlaw, he put off in a little pleasure launch. They had to thread the mine fields in the dark. An electric torch was turned on to check a compass bearing. A swell hit the boat and the torch fell among the supplies, throwing its beam upward. The guns of Corregidor roared. Everybody fell on the flashlight to smother it. Toward dawn they hit the channel between Luzon and Mindoro. They had a bad time but reached the headland of Mindoro and pulled into a cove. They hoped to work their way south through the Sulu Sea until clear of the Japanese and in touch with commercial transportation.

Hiding by day, traveling by night, after ten nights they reached Balabec across the Straits of Mindoro. Here they switched to a native sailboat. Jap naval patrols were out ahead; power-driven fishing boats, they learned, were being machine-gunned.

It took three days of bad weather to reach Sandakan, Borneo, where it was learned that the Japanese had captured the west coast of that island and were headed their way. They picked up a two-masted native sailing boat and a Moro crew. The sails ripped in the wind. With a mainsail improvised out of a tarp, the voyagers crossed the harbor, concealed by fog and rain, and hid in a swamp. The mate was sent to scurry up a small native boat of some kind; he didn't return. It was decided to send George Colley, swimming behind a log, to some nipa huts for the craft that they had to have, or perish.

George started down the stream, keeping watch for crocodiles, large water snakes, or whatever Borneo might have to offer. After swimming a mile or more, he espied another log in midstream. It disappeared. George recalled something from a previous jungle experience. "Being familiar with the actions and habits of crocodiles from my South American days, I knew that what had appeared to be a log was actually a crocodile. I was not pleased with the situation." The croc surfaced. George pushed his own log at him, made the bank in three strokes, and grabbed the root of a mangrove tree. He climbed twenty feet up. "There was Mr. Crocodile lying in the water with his snout on the river edge. The small waves lapping the shore caused the loose skin along the side of his mouth to wave up and down, showing an alternating pink and black color."

By moving along the branches of one tree to another, Colley reached an overhanging limb which gave a good view up and down the stream. The croc shifted his position along with the man. The man secured himself to the tree by his belt.

After some hours on that perch he was perceived by a boat-load of Japanese soldiers on patrol. They started throwing the bolts of their rifles. Colley came down.

The others of the party had been seized by another patrol. For a time all five were held in the maternity ward of the Sandakan Hospital, and a little something was done for the wound on George's hip. Then they were moved to an island. Seventy-nine men and fifty women and children had the use of one water faucet. After six weeks on a diet of rice, swamp grass, and doubtful fish, one-third of the prisoners were un-able to rise from their board beds.

To get food George discovered how to wriggle through the toilet seat of the latrine, out through the bucket service hole at the back, up a drain ditch to the fence, under that, and by a jungle trail over the backbone of the island to a Chinese leper colony on the other side. Here he found kindness and food of sorts. He opened a regular smuggling operation, bring-ing back coconuts, sugar cane, and the much-needed coconut or peanut oil which would ward off scurvy.

In 1943 the Colleys and their companions were moved to the large prisoner-of-war camp at Kuching. The camp had some 2,700 prisoners. Somebody rigged up a radio receiver and served up a weekly news bulletin, but he was caught and beheaded. Harry Webber was also among those executed. Prisoners of war died of starvation at the rate of a hundred a month; in July 1944, 189 died. All but four of 2,100 Australian prisoners were killed on death marches. The resourceful Colley found sugar syrup seeping through a warehouse floor and caught some of it in rusty cans.

On March 25, 1945, the prisoners saw a beautiful sight. Two four-engined Allied planes materialized out of a cloud. By July they were coming over every day. In August they came in low, doing circus stunts for pure jubilation. The war was over. But the prisoners were informed that the garrisons' tempers were short and all might be executed. Just when they were expecting a general slaughter, an Australian relieving column marched in.

When the Colleys reached Corregidor again, there was Steve Bechtel, awaiting the return of his stout-hearted lieutenant who'd said over the phone, "You won't hear from me again for about a month"—three years and nine months before.

There was reunion in the Erlander house in Oakland, too. Twelve hundred and forty-five M-K men had been captured on Wake. For four years Tooe and Olof had waited for this moment. And here, down out of the sky and down the plane's gangplank, he came. That night after the big dinner Tooe had prepared in the Oakland home, "Gee, Pa," Peter said—a tall, grave young man who had been through more than he cared to mention—"it really wasn't so bad. I had a book. A correspondence-school book on engineering. Know who'd lent it to me just before the Japs came? Mr. Morrison! It was the same one he'd learned from. I had four years with that book. Now I'm ready to go to work."

7

THE MANY-GABLED HOUSE OF KAISER

HENRY KAISER is the only man who can ride over highways of his own construction laid with cement of his own manufacture, skim along in a jeep of his own make, and zip over bridges whose metal his steel mills turned out from the original ore. He can view works of his building along the way—hospitals and dams, aluminum plants, and the stubs of notable shipyards. Today Henry J. shoots about Lake Tahoe at 105 miles an hour in his motorboat, or soaks up sun in Hawaii, while his son Edgar, Gene Trefethen, and the organization they built up carry the detailed burdens.

But the House of Kaiser is quite literally built on sand. Sand, that is, for concrete, along with rock and cement. A paving man and a purchaser of concrete aggregates before he ever was a dam builder or an "industrialist," he and his invaluable ally Tom Price (who still is with him) called on a big-scale aggregate producer in San Francisco back in 1922 to ask for a price to cover a job they were bidding. The sales manager, who kept them waiting an hour, occupied an office furnished at such obvious expense, and treated his visitors in such an airy manner, that Henry and Tom decided then and there to get into that profitable side line themselves. When a small paving job came up later, they discovered a fine sand and gravel deposit near it. That was their chance. They won the paving job and Price designed and built the plant. It was the laboratory which developed one-man handling of everything by push button in a lookout tower, the method which later made such a stir at Hoover.

That plant at Livermore, in the California Eastbay, is still the "main" aggregates plant in Kaiserdom and the cornerstone of its fortunes. It has produced, along with 5 million tons of material, some topflight executives. D. A. Rhoades, who today bosses the aluminum principality, there learned Kaiser methods. Edgar Kaiser and Gene Trefethen drove the gravel pit "dinkies." (Younger son, Henry Jr., got his own baptism in construction a little later—in the cement and steel plants and shipyards and aeronautical and artillery shell plants.) When Hoover Dam was in the offing, a structure whose aggregates definitely had to be produced at the site, the Kaiser organization sent its Tom Price to design and build the plant that automatically sorted, screened, cleaned, and mixed the dam's ingredients.

The vision of very large achievement came to Henry J. while Hoover Dam was abuilding. The spectacled man with the built-in dynamo and the flair for personal publicity was something of a legend before Hoover Dam was finished. "Hard worker, enthusiastic, lots of ideas," Dad Bechtel had tagged him.

The success with Bonneville Dam on the Columbia, followed by Grand Coulee in its second construction phase, gave Henry J. a grand feeling of omnipotence. When Coulee settled down to turning out horsepower, it contributed 40 per cent of all the energy used in the Northwest.

Shasta was third on the list of the new age of dams. Shasta was to hold back melting snows at the top of northern California, turn their falling water into power, check floods, and irrigate unawakened portions of the 400-mile central valley of the state. But here, as in the bidding for the first construction phase of Grand Coulee, the Six Companies took a belting. Before this, there had been yet another defeat which still causes the hides of old Six Companies' men to creep and twitch. For at the height of their prestige as Hoover Dam builders, the Six had also taken on a long vehicular tunnel back of Oakland, California. The Coast Range proved to be of shifting material pocketed with deadly gases, and the associates dropped the job at a loss of some $300,000. To their chagrin, an outfit of much slighter reputation picked up the task and carried it through. In the subsequent bidding for Shasta Dam, a last-minute $300,000 was added to the Six Companies' proposal. And when the bids were opened, the Six had lost $36 million Shasta by $263,000.

For Henry Kaiser, the beating in landing Shasta Dam had an important result. The sand-and-gravel man in him revolted at losing the prize completely, so he put in a bid for the materials that would go into the beautiful tall wedge. He got the contract for the sand and gravel and the nearly 6 million barrels of cement for $6,902,000, which was 29 cents a barrel less than his competition.

This was a gamble. Kaiser didn't have a cement plant. He only had an option on a hill of limestone overlooking Santa Clara Valley, south of San Francisco. With the contract in hand to provide cement for Shasta, and a dam in the Sierra known as Friant coming up for construction, he invited his Six Companies partners in as cement makers. They were dubious, but Henry was enthusiastic, just as he had been about Bonneville, and Bonneville had made them money; so some of them went along with his Permanente Cement Company. (The name came from a little stream that meandered through the hills.) Kaiser owned about 37 per cent of the new company; Utah, Shea, General Construction, and E. H. Heller each had 10 to 16 per cent; MacDonald & Kahn a twentieth, and Pacific Bridge a fraction. And he moved in on the purple brush-covered hills to build a cement plant.

The owners of Santa Clara Valley's villas and prune and apricot orchards were jarred at the very thought of billows of dust floating down over their roofs. Their holler was futile. The cement plant was the first big job for the dynamic battalion now known as the Kaiser Engineers. They set up their drawing boards right on the jobsite. Everything started at once. Hills were whacked off, industrial structures raised, rotary kilns hauled up the steeps, and a mile and a half of conveyor belts thrown into place. The gravitational pull on the belts was put to generating electric power to ply the machinery. Seven months from the start in '39, the first bag of cement was handed to Henry J. as a Christmas present. The plant cost about $7 million, made $844,000 in '41, almost doubled that in '42. It has been expanded under Wally Marsh's management, to a capacity of 8,500,000 barrels a year—more than a sack every second. Another plant in Southern California brings the total Kaiser production to 44 million sacks a year. The company owns Kaiser Gypsum Company, which operates wallboard and plaster plants, producing enough gypsum products to supply homes for a city of a quarter of a million every year. Some $44 million has been invested in cement facilities and $25 million for gypsum, and net earnings exceed $6,250,000 after taxes. That cement plant altered Henry Kaiser's whole career. He was off to the races,

and the draftsmen and the slide-rule boys were pantingly behind him—into magnesium, aircraft carriers, helicopters, into
steel and automobiles and aluminum and health plans. . . .

Magnesium, the extremely light metal, was rapidly com-
mending itself to industry, particularly in plane making, and
in 1940 it became apparent that a shortage would develop.
Up to then Dow Chemical was the only American producer
of magnesium. Kaiser and Harry Davis figured out that the
same natural gas being used to fire the big cement kilns could
be put to a second use in the production of magnesium; the
gas would even be enriched by using it to chill the magnesium. They hired Fritz Hansgirg, an Austrian refugee from
Hitler and the Japanese, who had built a magnesium plant
abroad using his carbothermic reduction process. The new
plant went up beside the cement plant in Santa Clara Valley.
There were lots of starting-up troubles, not the least because
Hansgirg's designs had been seized by the enemy and he had
to work from memory.

While the plant was producing 20 million pounds of magnesium, Kaiser's men came up with a brand-new product, called
"goop," which this plant alone produced. Goop, made by
mixing magnesium dust and oil, became the deadliest of
incendiary bomb materials, and the 82 million pounds of it
went into finishing the burning out of the industrial might of
Germany and Japan.

Kaiser Aluminum & Chemical have stayed with the production of magnesia, making it now out of dolomite and sea
water; using it as the raw material to manufacture refractories
at its firebrick factories. Men who gained wartime experience
in light metals went on to build the Kaiser Aluminum business.

About 1940, when he was still a sand-and-gravel man, a

cement man, and a contractor thinking about what to bid on next, Henry Kaiser fell to brooding about the basic metal of American industry. The Pacific coast had never had a full-scale blast furnace or an integrated steel mill. One of his very bright lieutenants, Chad Calhoun, warned him from Washington that steel was going to be the number one, hard-to-get requirement of the Pacific coast.

The West's war effort was being crippled by lack of steel, but when Kaiser asked the government to build a plant on the Coast, Washington told him "not one dime." Kaiser said, "We'll take the risk privately. We'll mortgage our earnings of three shipyards and the proposed plant, borrow, and build a steel mill." He borrowed the $109 million from RFC, later repaying in full, with interest. Soon at Fontana, east of Los Angeles, in a record-breaking matter of months, up went the blast furnace, open hearths, and rolling mill.

"Henry will come back to us," Felix Kahn remarked in '43. But Henry J. was an industrialist by that time—no longer just a contractor. (Henry and Edgar Kaiser, George Havas, *et al.*, feel strongly that they never did "leave" heavy construction. They have continued joint ventures and sponsorships, with some of the former Six Companies, and many more. Their present $638 million backlog of engineering and construction is heaviest in Kaiser Engineers' history. In 1956, in $138 million of heavy construction, they had among their partners on various projects Morrison-Knudsen, Pacific Bridge, General Construction, Walsh, Raymond Concrete, Perini, Bates & Rogers, W. J. Johnson Corp., Macco Corporation, and others.)

Meanwhile, in those war years, how the Kaiser organization did build ships! When somebody handed Henry a final report of shipbuilding dealings, it showed his total of that phase of the war effort as $4 billion. The sand-and-gravel man shook his head in awe.

8

BECHTEL EXTENDS HIS REACH

ON NOVEMBER 11, 1955, Harry and Ann Morrison threw a reunion party at San Francisco's Sheraton Palace for the long-dissolved Six Companies. The ranks of Hoover Dam's builders had thinned in twenty years, but several score constructors and wives were there within a bellhop's hop of the Palace Bar, where so much of the great dam had been planned, argued over, and practically erected on the polished walnut with dice and cocktail toothpicks.

Utah's Lester Corey reminisced, "It was the most wonderful organization of construction men ever put together. The joint venture that was organized at that time began the pattern that has been followed ever since." He recalled how Leland Cutler and Guy Stevick went East and induced the major bonding companies of the United States to enter into a similar joint-venture pattern with them and guarantee the Six Companies to Uncle Sam. How Harry Morrison, whose readiness to take on the hazards of a construction job has strewn the world with his works, shuddered at the very thought of entering a Las Vegas temple of chance, explaining —and meaning it—"I never gamble." How Felix Kahn would flip a coin with anybody for any sum, and always win—the coin that he used turning out to be the same on both sides. How Charley Shea saw some truck drivers in a general wild fist fight in front of a messhall at Boulder City, and cried, "I've got to look into that"—and did so, swinging his own fists with Gaelic joy; and when the police arrived, discovering that he had lost his hat but had acquired somebody's gold watch.

The reunion party ended to the strains of "Auld Lang Syne," Corey's nostalgic words ringing, "I wish we could start another dam just like it!"

But there never can be another Hoover because there can never be another First Big One. There can only be the wonderful medley of diverse projects given to the world by Hoover Dam because, while men were building it, it was building men. Steve Bechtel, for instance.

A figure of medium height who gives the impression of being taller, he is a personality of impact. Forehead and mouth are wide, chin and nose strong, smile ready and warming, hairline well out of the way. Skin and eye-wrinkles betray a lifetime of squinting at outdoor works under a bright sun. On a jobsite he likes to jam a wide-brimmed lightweight Panama on his high-domed head.

In his middle fifties he is a serious, deliberate man who manages, with very little stumbling, to walk with his head in the stars and his feet on solid ground.

He is Steve throughout his organization and it's a tribute. He is able to thump a man's back and give him hell at the same time, leaving the victim chastened, improved, and aware that he has just been through an experience. He has the art of choosing men and then making them responsible. He keeps his mental desk cleared.

In negotiation he has the quiet force of an atomic pile, as
two sheiks in the Arabian desert discovered when he wanted
to cross their jurisdictions with a pipeline. Since time began,
this pair or their ancestors had been at each other's throats in
one of those feuds that flourish where men are proud, prin-
cipled, and poor. Left to themselves, the current inheritors of
the feud would have passed it on to their successors for another millennium. The skilled American, with an interpreter,
managed to get the two into a tent. Then he went to work.
When he was done, the blood-feudists had chucked their
enmity in favor of Cadillacs and harmony, and brotherly love
had settled over the region for the first time in memory.

Steve was born in Indiana in 1900, rode a rough motorbike
for the Twentieth Engineers in World War I, and from there
went on to the University of California, where a number of
his future vice-presidents, then slim and trim and unsuspect-
ing, were also cracking calculus. Neither he nor his two brothers stayed to graduate.

As purchasing, transportation, and administrative officer
for the Six Companies on the Colorado River in the 1930s, he
sent for an old chum, Bill Waste, to assist when the equipment
salesmen came around, and now Bill is executive vice-president of Bechtel Corporation's activities wherever they extend.
After Hoover Dam and during the explosively expansive era
of public works that followed, Steve Bechtel was knitting his
thickening brows over what was next. He put into practice
what he calls being a "whole conception" thinker. He detected
something more congenial than simply bulldozing earth out
of the way, or beating one's brains out trying to underbid
the other fellow at a "letting." Why wait for a project to be
designed by others if he could anticipate and engineer it and

Mechanical camels in Arabia pull a ripper, and below, a close-up of the ripper blade.

The Arab finds the only spot of shade in miles of desert—Tapline.

Skyhook unloading Tapline pipe on Persian Gulf.

"Who called this a dry lake?"

Tapline goes on for 1,068 miles.

That's a rolling mill going up and that's Henry J.

Kaiser shipyards produced one-third wartime merchant tonnage.
Below, one of three blast furnaces at Fontana.

Kaiser Foundation Medical Center at Los Angeles.

be ready to put it together from ground breaking to front door key?

"I'll get the business," he said to his brothers Kenneth and Warren. "You be the financial man and you the construction man."

His plan was large and simple: He would make targets of big construction enterprises that judgment told him were ahead, study them in all their roundness, and be ready with practical plans and dependable estimates when the time came —in a position to talk real turkey. Steve decided to apply his "whole conception" thinking to the production of industrial energy, whether from oil, coal, falling water, or whatever the years might trot out. The thinking was evidently straight. A $20-million-a-year business had grown to a gross of fully $250 million, seven-eighths of it performed for less than a score of customers, all "steady"—certainly one of the most exclusive business clubs of this era, and one over which Steve exercises choosy selection.

It was the transport and refining of petroleum that early attracted him. For an associate he drew in John A. McCone, whom he'd known in undergraduate days at Berkeley and whose Consolidated Steel plant on the West Coast had furnished much of the steel for Hoover Dam. And he pulled in Ralph M. Parsons of Chicago, who had a highly specialized technical staff. (McCone and Parsons have since picked up their marbles and gone individual ways.)

By 1937 Bechtel-McCone-Parsons was building complex plants for oil and chemical companies in many places. Into these varied jobs moved Heinie Hindmarsh after twenty-four years of railroad engineering, shipbuilding, and heavy construction. Hindmarsh brought tested superintendents, foremen, and mechanics in his train. (One measure of a construc-

tion executive is ability to draw along able people with him.)
In moved Perry Yates, who'd been field engineer at Hoover
and Parker dams and who had also been with Shell in the
construction of oil refineries. Other figures entered the organization, men who gave it leadership for years to come. Relationships came into being with William V. McMenimen of
Raymond Concrete Pile; H. C. Price, the Bartlesville, Oklahoma, expert on electric welding; and Williams Brothers of
Tulsa, large-scale pipeline builders.

Here was a versatile gang, all set for joint venturing. Where
would they start?

It was a 125-kilometer, 16-inch pipeline known as the Mene
Grande, in Venezuela. Contracts also involved dock construction and telephone lines, and harbor and wharf installations
at Ciudad Bolívar for the Venezuelan government.

With its 40 miles of Mototan-Mene Grande highway to be
hacked through jungles, and the aches and pains of equatorial
construction generally, all this was a fairish chore, and George
S. Colley, Jr., was sent down to run the performance. Although many things were ahead for George, and none of them
exactly on the quiet side, he was to look back on Mene
Grande as the toughie, and wince when he thought about its
snakes, heat, humidity, and fish that darted with razor-blade
teeth at human ankles.

Five jobs in the first two years, each different, showed the
new Bechtel technology—plants for Standard of California;
engineering and construction of a refinery in Montana; a
plant for Union Oil; for Hercules Powder Company an ammonia plant. Meanwhile W. A. Bechtel Company, the trunk
organization, continued to build pipelines and railroads.
The pipelines ran across the plateaus of Wyoming and
through the canyons of Utah, and a network of them began

furrowing the citrus orchards of Southern California. Came war, and with John McCone bossing Calship at Los Angeles and Kenneth Bechtel running Marinship at Sausalito, the Bechtel shipyards turned out 2,274,000 displacement tons of shipping. An offshoot of the activities of the period was the construction of Canol pipeline in the Far North, from the MacKenzie River to Alaska—a military-inspired project performed by Bechtel-Price-Callahan under a sort of shotgun-wedding arrangement, with army brass setting a 4-inch diameter for the long pipe. The contractors put the pipe down as required, but when the war ended and it was realized that tankers in peacetime could carry oil to Alaska more cheaply, the line was pulled up. Bechtel and McCone also built a huge modification center in Alabama, where bombers were readied for combat.

Came along a 170-mile pipeline in Montana, a 270-mile line in Illinois and Indiana, and, for variety, an ice-skating rink at Berkeley, California, where some national figure-skating championships were held. Connoisseurs of skating admired the contestants, but any engineering eyes present were caught by the tremendous clear-span roof.

By this time the Bechtel interests were all over the map in heavy industrial construction, with engineering and design leading the way. Three Bechtel-built open-pit copper mines with their processing plants pockmarked the Southwest. And during the war years, in addition to other activities that were not small, Bechtel-McCone produced fourteen oil refineries, besides starting two others—at Curaçao in the West Indies and on the island of Bahrain in the Persian Gulf. The outfit in group partnership with others built breakwaters and docks along the Pacific, cleaned out Miraflores lock in the Panama Canal, dammed the Arkansas River, and built some mystery storage tanks at Hanford, Washington, which turned out to be for the plutonium that announced itself over Hiroshima.

During the war years the Bechtel interests were also in many shows run by the Six Companies' components. Bechtel-McCone owned nearly one-fifth of Kaiser's Permanente Metals, which in turn owned those Kaiser-run Richmond shipyards. Bechtel-McCone owned 20 per cent of an Evansville, Indiana, shipyard, 9 per cent of Kaiser-run Cregonship, and 9 per cent of Hendy.

War's end found the Bechtel brothers personally ready to bow out of engineering-construction. All three did just that, leaving key men to carry on.

And carry on these men did; stuff came thick and fast. Refineries and more refineries; a plant for H. J. Heinz at Tracy, California, to process a hundred tons of tomatoes a minute; pipelines from hither to yon and from this-away to that; a "mill of tomorrow" for General Mills at Los Angeles, which can make anything from breakfast cereal to soup; and, from '45 onward, a cycle of engineering and construction for the utilities that was to produce hundreds of millions' worth of plants within ten years. In its variety about the only thing lacking was a tomato catsup pipeline from Tracy, California, to Heinz's headquarters in Pennsylvania.

Stephen Davison Bechtel stayed out of construction for one year. Then he charged back, like a fire horse snorting for his harness. He acquired the principal interest in Bechtel-McCone and made it into Bechtel Corporation, the entity which today, as a corporate partnership of key men, operates a far-flung show of construction subsidiaries and enterprises. It goes in for jobs of scope and vision that can be organized, completed, and handed over to the owners ready to operate—no manufacturing empire like Kaiser's for this group. Steve's fellow directors in Bechtel Corporation are his brother Kenneth, his son Steve, Jr., and his valuable ally and general counsel, Robert L. Bridges; veteran constructors George Colley, John M. Rogers, Bill Waste, Perry Yates, John Kiely, Jerry Komes, and John L. Simpson, who chairmans the finance committee.

The group runs its affairs with considerable invisibility and a deafening silence—although, after all, its feats are pretty conspicuous. It often lines up in co-ventures with Morrison-Knudsen, J. H. Pomeroy, Conyes Construction, Hawaiian Dredging, Raymond, Kiewit, and George Wimpey of London. A rundown of four years to July 15, 1955, suggests that the value of Bechtel-supervised or Bechtel-constructed projects was over $1 billion. The percentages of work were refinery, chemical and process plants, 35; pipelines, 22; power generation and distribution, 21; industrial and mining, 22.

A big share of Interprovincial Pipeline from Canada's Alberta field to the Great Lakes, followed by the Lakehead Extension, which involved a daring underwater crossing of the Straits of Mackinac, fell to Bechtel's engineers and constructors. And to a combine of Canadian Bechtel, Mannix, and Oklahoma Contracting Co. of Dallas came, in 1955, the behemoth of gas pipelines to date, the Trans-Canada. This 2,350-mile steel hose, a lot of it 34 inches in diameter, dives under 110 rivers and lakes and 240 creeks, Alberta to Ontario and way places. The diameter of that pipeline, though staggering, didn't throw the Bechtel staff off stride. They'd built a 34-incher 500 miles for Pacific Gas & Electric in California in 1950. Out West, Canadian Bechtel, with Steve, Jr., in charge, brought Peace River gas from Northern Alberta and British Columbia through a 30-inch, 650-mile line to warm the blood and spin the wheels of British Columbia and the

U. S. Northwest. In this enterprise the third generation of the Dad Bechtel brood, now about the age that Steve was when Hoover Dam started, has received the accolade from Mr. Pipeliner himself—"Stevie is a real pipeliner."

The emphasis today in the Bechtel shop is, more than ever, complete turn-key projects. Steve describes it this way: "Bechtel Corporation is primarily an engineering-construction organization. It is not concerned with operating the projects it designs and builds. There is no outside ownership and therefore it is remarkably free from outside pressures. The company offers a completely integrated service—everything from preliminary study to the delivery of a completed plant or pipeline—and it also performs any of the individual services separately. A recent development is management service. In this form of operation all project activities are co-ordinated under Bechtel direction. The term for this is 'Managers of Engineering and Construction.' Three key points which interest major industrial customers are quality of the job, its cost, and speed of completion." As managers of engineering and construction delivering quality within the budget, the Bechtel formula has had a world-wide workout.

Bechtel headquarters are still in San Francisco, but no one building holds them. Operations are handled from a central control point in Mills Tower, a downtown office building, where Bill Waste is the skipper on the flying bridge; but the firm's 2,700 engineers, technicians, and helpers overflow into eight more nearby office buildings and there are probably others still to be discovered, nested away somewhere. Around the corner from Mills Tower is a twelve-story structure owned by Industrial Indemnity, the insurance company whose chairman is Kenneth Bechtel, and on the twelfth floor of this white shaft is the sunny view-office of Stephen D. It is a map-hung room with an acre or so of desk, shaped like a flatiron, with the broad end for his elbows.

In this room many of the studies are launched which have a way of becoming realities in cement and steel, and which eventually alter the economies and habits of peoples. The medicine made in this room is global brew. But much of the brew is made not here but in the field. The man and his Panama hat are away about half the year, traveling from one circus site to the next. His Lodestar planes are always gassed up and ready. And wherever he goes, his wife Laura, in the true construction-life tradition, goes with him. Steve is good for 125,000 to 150,000 miles of far-ranging per year, his key men are 100,000-milers or better, and a good idea of how they spread-eagle the field may be seen from the fact that on one sample day in 1957 seven of these key men were in seven different places on the globe, arranging new details of this world's face-lifting.

To carry out the imaginative concepts of Steve and the men around him, the stem corporation has many subsidiaries. Two, with names as similar as Theodora and Dorothea, were Bechtel International Corporation and International Bechtel, Inc. They were put together shortly after war's end, BIC to operate within the United States on engineering, design, and procurement for foreign jobs, and IBI to gather up some old, tried co-venturers for partners and do the actual foreign field engineering and construction. Latterly, International Bechtel Builders, Inc., has unfurled its flag and has a large field of operations in the Middle East, and a number of other corporations have been developed to handle other foreign commitments as they arise.

This is a period of transition for Bechtel, with younger men coming to the fore. It is mostly home-grown talent that is taking over. Chief among these is Steve, Jr., and it does not take any great shrewdness on the part of an observer to detect that he will soon be at the wheel. The old-timers agree that he has what it takes.

In 1948 Carl Erlander, twenty-three and head of a family of his own by this time, came home and told his wife, who'd been Janie Lloyd, "Honey, we're going to Arabia for Bechtel!"

"I'm going to have another baby," mentioned Janie. "Or didn't you know?"

"I hear people have babies in Arabia, too," said Carl. "But if you say we mustn't go——"

"I didn't say it," stated Janie promptly. "I'm the wife of a pipeliner. Do we leave in two days, or in ten minutes?"

9

UTAH HATCHES ITS OWN EGGS— AND OTHERS

PEPE and Jorge Pilar, fishermen whose ancestors were among those Incas overthrown by the Spanish conquistadors, were paddling about in a shallow indentation known as San Juan Bay, 240 miles south of El Callao in the Department of Ica.

The coast of Peru tends to be a treeless strip, visited by mist and wind but seldom by rain. Thirty miles back, the Andes rear their arid foothills and lofty heads. Jorge and Pepe's home was a tiny Indian village up on the beach. The sight of a school of bonita in the empty bay, on this January morning of 1953, would have delighted them; the fin of a sailfish would have made the day one for thanking the Inca gods and the saints. What they actually beheld was much more memorable —it was dumfounding. A modern ship, decks loaded, came around the headland and dropped anchor. Nothing bigger than a guano carrier had ever done that before in this vicinity.

Landing craft belonging to the Peruvian navy, and loaned for a peaceful invasion, were lowered over the side. Into them went boxes and drums and bales, bulldozers, a power shovel, a crane—things the humble fishermen had never heard of. What was happening?

Within sixteen weeks the village up on the beach was a permanent city of several thousand people with all the trimmings of schools, hospital, churches; was on its way to becoming the chief port for tonnage in all Peru.

It was a part of the saga of Utah Construction Company, wasteland developers whose antecedents in desert-busting extended back more than a hundred years.

When W. H. and E. O. Wattis, risk-takers and builders to the end, were both struck down during Hoover Dam's construction, the leadership of their Utah Construction Company passed to well-trained hands. It built Davis Dam farther down the Colorado; built concrete siphons and canals on the aqueduct between Parker Dam and Los Angeles; built the Geneva Steel plant at Provo, Utah; sponsored a major section of the Delaware River water tunnel for the city of New York; and built highways in Alaska.

Utah until 1945 had continued to operate large ranches. The feel for land and livestock had never left the descendants of the sage land pioneers, whose construction operations in the early days had been dependent on horses, mules, and feed for stock and men. The company owned a 7,000-acre ranch near Oakdale, California, and 550,000 acres in Nevada-Utah. Supplemented by lands leased from railroad and government, the total acreage on which ranching operations were conducted was over one million.

But with the substitution of diesel fuel for hay and oats, the company sold its ranches. It came down out of the range lands and placed its active headquarters in San Francisco. The lobby of its acreage of offices at 100 Bush Street is decorated with an outsized mural of Hoover Dam. Utah never forgets that it provided the first and third presidents of the Six Companies and 20 per cent of the capital for that group.

Allen D. Christensen, top-flight engineer, is now Utah's president; Marriner S. Eccles its chairman. (In recognition of the company's modern role as a city feller, the year 1956 found Utah's alert young executive vice-president, Edmund Wattis Littlefield, serving as president of the San Francisco Chamber of Commerce.) All three are of direct line of descent from the company's founders and early supporters.

The company operates on a large scale in the field of open-pit mining. Utah had been doing work for mining companies since its early days and in this respect it occupied a unique position. It continues to show up as a challenger in competitive bidding, and it regularly participates in joint ventures sponsored by the others, but it is also disposed to buy and develop, and to guard what it owns.

Currently or in the recent past, this constructor built the far-flung installations for Kennecott Copper Corporation at Bingham, Utah, and zinc fuming plants for American Smelting and Refining Company in Texas, Mexico, and California; joint-ventured into rice production for the Republic of Indonesia; served as consultant to the Korea Tungsten Mining Company, which is owned by the Republic of Korea; and carried out in Alaska, with Bechtel and J. H. Pomeroy & Co., $27 million worth of military installations. Alone, it also is builder of several hundred miles of the Alcan military highway. It co-ventured on highways and canals in Colombia; aided in development of Toquepala copper mine, two miles high, in the Peruvian Andes; built dams in California. It diversified by taking an active part in residential building. In 1952–54 Utah participated, in various places, in the construction of several thousand homes.

The company also acquired 5,000 acres east of Oakland, California, in the Moraga Valley—a site once granted by the

Mexican government to early-day Spanish Californians, and won away from its grantees in a poker game. The gambler later left the region just ahead of a lynching party. Here Utah announced its intention to lay out some $200 million on housing and transportation for 30,000 people. Because the neighbors had not been forewarned and prepared, they emitted stricken screams at the thought of so much new congestion and threatened to block the enterprise. Utah, fresh from the wide open spaces and lacking so much as a press agent, let alone a "director of public relations," could only listen in bewilderment to the uproar and remain speechless. However, the pressure of $200 million is pretty irresistible, and so is the pressure of the need for housing.

In addition to the Moraga project, the company went over the hills and down to San Francisco Bay and set about enlarging the island and city of Alameda. Its second century finds it heavily engaged in the manufacture of land by hydraulic fill on various fringes of San Francisco Bay. On this bay the suction dredge was invented, back in the seventies.

The vigorous fellow in the western cowman's boots and the construction stiff's helmet also sponsored a $58 million joint venture in copper at San Manuel, Arizona; drilled a 17,000-foot tunnel near Ogden; explored coal seams in Navajo Indian Reservation, New Mexico; performed strip mining at Iron Mountain in Utah; and participated in erection of navy barracks at Guam. He operates in Canada, Panama, Australia, and Okinawa. A joint venture was construction of a major Ford assembly plant at Milpitas, California.

This was the outfit which disturbed the calm of fishermen Pepe and Jorge Pilar that day in '53 in San Juan Bay.

In 1905 an engineer, Federico Fuchs, had picked up tales

of *La Montaña del Iman*—the Mountain of the Magnet—in southern Peru. With a prospector named Justo Pastor, he'd headed for this reputed lodestone and he'd located it. The site was less than 20 miles from the sea.

In that year 1905 the need for iron ore from overseas for United States furnaces was something for the remote future. Peru was left to hug its nugget and bide its time.

But the mountain was recalled when Minnesota's Mesabi began to show bottom. In the early 1940s the Peruvian government set up an organization called Corporacion Peruana del Santa. It was decided to engage a competent U.S. company to lease and manage the development. Santa got in touch with Utah Construction in San Francisco and Allen Christensen, in 1952, went down for a look and took a nine-month option agreement with the Santa Corporacion. In this short period Utah would have to test the deposit, find a market, and develop the financing. The remoteness, 300 miles south of Lima in a region virtually without roads, called for investment beyond Utah's scope. And with extensive new ore sources being developed in Venezuela, Liberia, and Labrador, buyers of Peruvian ore might be hard to find.

But what Utah's diamond drill boys and aeromagnetic surveyors found looked very good. The deposits covered an area 12 miles by 18. Over 70 million tons of commercial ore appeared to be in sight. Yet, at the end of its nine months, Utah had turned up only U. S. Steel as a seriously interested customer, and that interest was confined to 1953 and the early months of 1954, after which Big Steel's Orinoco ore would be in production. This meant that the Mountain of the Magnet would have to disgorge early in '53 if it was to start with any assured business. And not only capital but physical equipment were going to be hard to get, owing to postwar shortages.

But Utah decided that the United States was going to need that ore and need it badly, that money and equipment had to be found, and that the whole show must get into production within months. On New Year's Eve, 1952, Christensen reached an agreement with U. S. Steel calling for initial ore deliveries in April and full production by September. This task involved risks that would have stirred the pulses of the old Wattis brothers, for it was in the true Utah tradition. If the mine failed to produce by April, demurrage charges on the waiting ships would be tremendous, and Utah would have to supply the promised ore by rail from its mine at Cedar City, Utah—a treatment that more properly belonged to gold.

Utah went to work.

It invited the Cyprus Mines Corporation, a distinguished American name in mining, to join in. The Marcona Mining Company, jointly owned by Utah and Cyprus, was the result. The project was laid before the Export-Import Bank. A loan of $2,500,000 was obtained. The balance of the capital was supplied by Utah and Cyprus. There began to look like big things ahead for the land of the Incas.

In January 1953, the location of the ore bodies was still a desert. The only use this waste was being put to was a government guano-mining operation on a headland. The region for a million years had been strictly for the feathered flocks of the sea. Nothing was at hand for large-scale human use. No fresh water was closer than 60 kilometers.

But four months from landing day, such was the speed put on by the *Yanquis* from the North, the Mountain of the Magnet was spewing ore and U.S. furnaces a thousand miles away were gulping it. Busses painted bright orange, the

Marcona and Utah color, hauled men to and fro. Over everything hung ocher-hued ore dust and the air throbbed with Yankee din.

By that time a new city for 3,000 people had sprung up behind the bench. Potable water was provided by the treatment of sea water—a distilling plant for a whole town. Up on the Mountain of the Magnet ore was coming out in 6-yard bites. A sign, bright yellow, with large red letters, lightheartedly proclaimed LOS ANGELES CITY LIMITS. SAN FRANCISCO, 5,965 MILES. And down to San Juan the ore was coming in 22-wheel truck trailers. Working personnel, exclusive of families, numbered 1,200, about sixty of whom were from the United States. Within a year cat skinners, drivers, and shovel operators were Peruvian. The locals had been trained to new skills and were drawing unheard-of wages.

Eleven million American dollars had been expended. Ships were being loaded at a clip of a thousand tons an hour. They were leaving at a rate of better than one every other day for the U. S. Steel plants at Morrisville, Pennsylvania, or Mobile, Alabama. During the first year 164 ships tied to San Juan's dock. One year and seven months from L day, Peru occupied third place as iron-ore supplier to the States.

But by the fall of 1954, Orinoco and Labrador ore had come into the market and it looked as if Utah's Peruvian gamble was doomed after all. The view became even more dismal when U. S. Steel, glutted with ore from other sources, asked deferment of part of the Peruvian schedule into 1955. But courage paid off. The market for Peruvian ore picked up. Bethlehem Steel entered into a long-term agreement. Before the year ended Marcona had eighteen customers including German mills as well as American, and two new 32,000-ton ore carriers had been ordered built and two more chartered.

Today the company port at San Juan handles more tonnage than any other port in Peru. The sales of iron ore are responsible for approximately 10 per cent of the foreign exchange earnings of the country. In the northern part of Peru at Chimbote the government has under way the construction of a steel mill using electric furnaces served by power that will be developed in the area. Marcona will provide the ore. Says Allen Christensen, "There is a great need for construction services in foreign lands to raise the standards of living of the people and to take fuller advantage of unused natural resources."

Pepe Pilar operates a power shovel now, shouting with glee as it bites into the mountain, and Jorge drives a fine orange-colored bus. Their houses have electric appliances and their children go to school.

But sometimes, on a Sunday, Jorge and Pepe steal away from it all, push their boat out, and go fishing, hoping to regain some of the solitude that has been lost, and maybe even to see a sailfish.

In 1954, when it appeared certain that co-operation would be established between Canada and United States on the construction of the St. Lawrence seaway and power project, Utah joined with Morrison-Knudsen Co., B. Perini & Sons, Walsh Construction Company, Peter Kiewit & Sons, and a Canadian group to participate in bidding on all the work of major consequence on this momentous undertaking. They obtained the Long Sault Dam, the U.S. half of the Barnhart Island powerhouse, and the Grass River Lock. The Long Sault Dam contract, in the amount of almost $26 million, is being prosecuted with the resources of all partners, as is the Barnhart Island powerhouse contract at $36 million. Walsh Construction

Company sponsors the work on Long Sault; Perini & Sons sponsors Barnhart.

In 1954 the same group, with the exception of Kiewit, won the Massena Intake.

Besides building Big Eildon Dam in Australia, discussed in Chapter 18, Utah is currently in Europe with technical assistance, helping lift into place Serre Poncon Dam. In '52 Electricite de France, the national commission for electric generation and transmission, began planning this dam in southern France. Because the foundation was suitable only for an earth- and rock-fill structure and Utah had the experience, Compagnie Industrielle de Travaux of Paris asked Utah to send over a couple of consultants. When the government agency subsequently invited bids from French contractors, it was specified that all proposals should be made in collaboration with a suitable American firm. A joint venture of four French contractors, with Utah as a partner to furnish supervision and technical assistance, was the result. So the cowboy, miner, and railroad grader waxed his mustache, pulled on spats, and went continental. Serre Poncon Dam, 20 million cubic yards of earth and cobbles, is now rising 400 feet above the Durance River in southern France, its two 30-foot diversion tunnels turning the river, and a "glory hole" spillway tunnel and underground powerhouse going in. No dam on the European continent is as sizable, and this collaboration of an American contractor with French firms in hydroelectric development on French soil is unique.

The episode would probably cause the shade of E. O. Wattis, riding his ghostly horse across that trestle in the sagebrush country, to lift his sombrero and wave it. He lived in a land of wide horizons, and would be delighted to see that his descend-

ants and successors are climbing to where they can get an
even wider sweep.

Utah has long been flipping back and forth over the border
of Mexico like a commuter, developing mines and a hundred
other works. Lately it undertook two more, in connection with
what Mexico's President Cortines calls "The March to the
Sea." As a country with some 8,000 miles of coast line, Mexico
has always been aware of its maritime potential. It dates back
to the days when the annual galleon from the Philippines,
laden with the treasures of the Orient, used to sight North
America at Cape Mendocino on the California coast and feel
its way down until it could reach Acapulco and tie up to a
tree.

In 1952 Cia. Utah, S.A., Utah Construction Company's
Mexican subsidiary, was called in on a program which will
ultimately open the way for the agricultural and mineral
wealth of the Mexican cornucopia to reach world markets.

Cia. Utah was given the responsibility for developing two
principal Pacific ports, Guaymas and Mazatlán.

Many years ago Guaymas almost sprang into the commercial spotlight when American railroad barons were fighting
each other. In the 1880s the Santa Fe built the Sonora Railway out of Guaymas and up the coast of the Gulf of California and announced its intention of making that port the
outlet for transcontinental freight. It was but a move in the
intricate chess game that millionaires were playing, and re-
sulted in Southern Pacific hurriedly granting its rival large
favors elsewhere. After that, in spite of further rail laying
from gringo-land southward, Guaymas slept in the sun. A
luxury hotel for fishermen and tourists was its chief activity.
But lately it found itself backed by newly developed agricul-

tural areas in the state of Sonora, the country's breadbasket. Irrigation works on the Yaquí and Mayo rivers and wells in the Hermosillo and Guaymas valleys had done it.

To make way for new docks and concrete-paved storage areas, Utah knocked over and moved an obstacle known as The Mountain of the Squirrel. It cost $2,700,000 to move the mountain as part of a $16 million development, but Guaymas abruptly came to life. Within 19 months the port was doing $5 million worth of shipping a year. That is considered only a starter.

Down at Mazatlán, one of the world's beautiful harbors, Cia. Utah is also busy. This town serves an extremely fertile area and is now coupled with the central plateau region by the new Durango-Mazatlán railroad and the new highway following the same route, as well as the elderly Sud Pacifico de Mexico, built years ago by Utah's forces. Cia. Utah threw two breakwaters around the entrance to Mazatlán Bay that make it possible for 12,000-ton vessels to steam in. Previously 2,000 tons was the limit and larger craft had to lie well off shore and handle passengers and goods by lighter.

It looks as if vigorous days are ahead for Mexico's west coast.

The long-striding boots of the Utah Construction Company have also taken it in recent months to East Pakistan, where a multipurpose dam and hydroelectric power plant are going up on the Karnafuli River. The completed project will provide numerous benefits to the province, which is about the size of Alabama but with a population fifteen times greater. It will produce power for processing and manufacturing plants and home use, provide flood control, irrigation, and reclamation benefits, bolster food production, make accessible a thousand square miles of virgin forests, and facilitate river navigation.

The $30,500,000 Utah contract represents $24,500,000 in foreign exchange financed by the International Cooperation Administration, and the rupee equivalent of $6,500,000 provided by Pakistan. The remainder of the ultimate $63 million total estimated cost of the project will represent additional rupees to be invested by Pakistan.

Few American taxpayers will ever see this big earth-filled dam 30 miles above Chittagong on the Bay of Bengal, but for that matter they seldom see the works they have helped finance at home, either.

10

MORRISON SHOVES MORE MOUNTAINS

IN BOISE, Idaho, one daybreak in 1952, Morrison-Knudsen's boss buyer and storekeeper awoke to the jangle of his phone, and his heels hit the floor with practiced speed. Trouble somewhere. And trouble it was. Down in California, at 4:52 A.M., there had been an earthquake. It centered in the Tehachapi Mountains where the long freight trains of Southern Pacific and Santa Fe jointly use one set of tracks for snaking the immensely important food products of the San Joaquin Valley south and east to the nation's tables. The steep mountains had been twisted about, tunnels had caved in, and embankments had slid down hill.

Jim Wells, M-K's vice-president and district manager at Los Angeles, had put in that call to Boise. How much earth-moving machinery could the outfit lay its hands on right away? Mark Robinson, the man who'd been heaved out of bed, could answer that one—he was virtually a human IBM machine. A clearheaded and slightly harassed-looking man with receding hair and a flat belly, he was known as General Superintendent of Equipment. Of the 3,700 major construction machines and 3,000 other sizable items owned by the company, most of it was at work in eighty-five going projects in the U.S. and Alaska; but if Jim was really in a hurry in a whole-sale way, Mark knew where he could rent rigs in quantity all over several states. With or without operators. Out of that reservoir and M-K's standby supply he would be pleased to meet Jim's request. That was fine, yelled Jim Wells; what he wanted at once, down here 998 road miles from Boise, was a hundred pieces of heavy equipment, to be followed within hours by seventy-five more; and would Mark please get those wheels and engines turning first and pull his pants on after-ward. Jim hung up, aware that he had just put in the rush order for a concentration of earth-moving gear that was close to a North American record.

In other days Santa Fe and Southern Pacific would have straightened out their tangled tracks strictly by their own ef-forts. They would have pushed all visitors down the bank and summoned their bull wreckers, gandy dancers, and big hooks from Oregon's border to Mexico's, and after a deal of swear-ing, sweating, and h'isting they'd have opened the line, though the job was about like digging the Panama Canal. But the thing that counted now was *time*. The month was July, the produce of the great western farms was perish-able, and all alternative routes were roundabout. Morrison-Knudsen were specialists at earth moving and at railroad maintenance; this major-sized earthquake was their tiger, and they could come and handle it.

Mark Robinson was accustomed to surprise orders. Hadn't M-K engineers on a tunnel project under faraway Boston just come up with a request for five locomotives, and hadn't they been delivered? Mark had had three idle at the moment in Spokane, two more in Boise; the five were on their way east quicker than Boston men could dump a case of tea. So he tackled this new request, which was for $3 million worth of earth-shoving stuff, most of it to be on its way before breakfast.

Others of the M-K staff had likewise been tumbled out of bed: Jack Bonny, general manager; Murray Burns, railway maintenance expert; the whole employment staff. Calls went out for cat skinners and tunnel men all over the West. H. L. Leventon, who was assigned to be project manager, was off on a fishing trip. It took Forest Service telephones to find him, but found he was, and hauled out of the woods and flown to the Tehachapis practically with his rubber waders still on. Lev had been top boss of Red Hill underground work in Hawaii, among other items of a moleman's career.

Tehachapi Pass is one of the bottlenecks of the continent. Keeping it open is a railroad "must," though doing so is often a problem. Cloudbursts have been known to engulf and bury a locomotive out of sight under tons of silt; shifting rock structure has tossed rails out of line; the heat that surges down from the Mojave Desert sometimes warps the rails. At the time of this earthquake, the track climbed to a half-mile altitude through fourteen tunnels in such tight spirals that the engine sometimes seemed to be trying to swallow the caboose.

Within hours the hard-hat boys and the gear-jammers of a hundred digging, boring, and earth-shoving jobs had converged on the Tehachapis. Together with sixteen well-equipped gangs provided by the railroads, they lifted a quarter million cubic yards of earth out of two cuts; lifted the tops completely from two of the smashed tunnels, letting the daylight in; and partially daylighted another. The concrete shells of the tunnels were smashed to rubble by 3-ton steel balls swung against them, and power shovels, draglines, and dynamite did the rest. The longest tunnel was so badly wrecked that its owner, the S.P., decided to abandon it. A new grade was ordered that would take future trains out and around the mountain. So a shoofly, or temporary grade and track, went in. These required a fill in length and height that was about the equivalent of a causeway across the Golden Gate. In 150 hours the giant cuts and fills were in place for the 4,358-foot bypass. Twenty-four days after the quake, a diesel-powered freight rolled over the new grade and the line was open.

At the moment the Tehachapi quake came, M-K was also reasonably busy pushing mountains around in many other places, and kept right on doing so. As on Sherman Hill west of Cheyenne, Wyoming.

When the first transcontinental railroad was being built in the 1860s, its arrival at Cheyenne had been a historic moment. Cheyenne was 516 miles from Omaha, with 516 still to go to the junction with the Central Pacific, building eastward from the Coast. Six thousand railroad-graders and tie-tampers turned night into day at the midpoint construction town and the roaring camp wasn't quieted down until a vigilance committee appeared with some suitably knotted rope-ends. Soon after that the mule-pounders and rail-layers were gone, moving steadily westward over land that was apparently level—or so the human eye considered. But the puffing little 30-ton locomotives which had to climb those rails knew better. Under their wheels was a grade, steady and relentless, and the grade was still there eighty-five years later, when locomotives had grown to 400 tons. In 33 miles of original line, the road climbed 2,201 feet. There its tracks stood at the summit of the continental divide. The spot had been named Sherman, "in honor of General Sherman," said an old-time Overland tourist guide, "the tallest general in the service." Seventy miles to the southwest was Long's Peak, and 165 miles to the south was Pike's Peak, both visible. The air was thin, and in winter was bitingly sharp; rains and snows rode the east wind, heavy storms swept up from the southwest, and temperatures sometimes dropped to 30 below.

Such was the top of the United States for the eight and a half decades through which the Union Pacific endured Sherman Hill, though whittling at it year by year. But by the middle of the twentieth century the big road's managers finally decided that the hill still was too steep. They'd brought the grade down to 1.52 per cent and it was still a fuel-eater. What the railroad would be charmed with was something like, say, 0.82 per cent, even though it meant whacking the continental divide off at the knees.

Having decided, the railroad found itself in a hurry. Every day and hour meant fuel, meant wear and tear on rolling stock, meant time in the competitive business of rushing freight and passengers east and west. And the railroad could now depend upon modern technology to do what black powder and the hand-shovel tarriers couldn't do back in '67. The job went to M-K, which had performed its first contract for Union Pacific thirty years before and had long been equipped to deliver specialized service in railroad building.

The job entailed a 42-mile line change, one of the major pieces of U.P. grading since the golden spike of the transcontinental line was driven. The new line would cost millions and would be 9 miles longer than the old, but would save 15 minutes each way. The U.P. set February 18, 1952, for the starting date of the regrading, with eighteen months to go. But a shorter time would be appreciated.

Six hundred M-K men piled in, during the gales of February and March, riding $3,140,000 worth of machinery.

They separated into eight "spreads," adjusted their ear muffs, blew into the wrists of their mittens, and went to work. On the western portion, in Granite Cañon where the earlier builders had quarried out the stone for the town of Cheyenne, air hammers set up a chattering. Dynamite began heaving the scenery around, and 120,000 tons of rock ballast came out. In there and elsewhere moved the power shovels and the 15- and 20-yard dump trucks, each good for the contents of a small knoll at a trip. Everybody hurried—it was the easiest way to keep warm. And 111 major fills began to rise. The highest fill was 164 feet, and the deepest cut was 165 feet. Also, 500 culverts went into place. Some of them weren't ordinary drainpipes. One was 15 feet in diameter, through which a couple of well-laden trucks could pass in opposite directions with plenty of room for the drivers to insult each other.

Winter turned to spring. Wildflowers and human ears came out of hiding. Spring turned to summer and in that sizzling desolation the crews thought longingly of those nice, cool blizzards that used to roar down off Pike's Peak. Tehachapi rocked a thousand miles away, and M-K handled that too, but Sherman Hill went right on dropping down to grade. Autumn, and the spreads were knocking down and hauling away a million cubic yards a month. Winter, and they were still at it. Behind them, practically walking up their backs, came the heavy steel into place. The earlier-day tracklayers, those who had laid iron up and over old Sherman Hill, had curved their slender 30-pound rails, when a curve was necessary, by placing the rail ends on a couple of rocks and jumping on the suspended middles. Tracklaying has since become more mathematical.

In twelve months, instead of the contracted eighteen, the job was done. The big earth-shoving machines moved away to other tasks, of which Morrison always has scores going at once. And today the freights and passenger trains of the U.P. whip over the divide that scarcely anybody knows is there.

From the top of the Rockies down to Great Salt Lake is a long glide that finds a spidery trestle extending across that inland sea. Built in 1904, straight as a chalk line for nearly 23 miles, the single-track trestle had since been partly filled in until only a dozen miles of airy piling remained. But those were 12.6 real miles which M-K tackled in 1956 with a flotilla of tugs, dredges, and barges and enough more specialized equipment to represent $15 million and about 600 men. When completed three years hence, the solid roadbed will enable Southern Pacific trains to hurtle across in fast streamliner time. Some of the equipment involved includes barges 250 feet long and 55 feet wide, each capable of carrying 2,000 yards of material; tremendous power shovels; and a 2½-mile conveyor system hurtling 3,500 tons an hour along on a 54-inch-wide belt.

11

AFGHANISTAN—DIKE OF FREEDOM

AN AREA remote as a star but big as Texas lies between Soviet Russia and the warm-water oceans. This area is Afghanistan. Its mountains are high. Its people, though tough, are few. Poverty, war, and threats of invasion are an old story to this folk. Today the bulldozers and shovels of an American contractor are working hard and fast to beef up the Afghans' economy.

After ten years and tens of millions of American dollars expended, wasted waterpower will be turned into energy, it is hoped, and useful industries will develop. Hundreds of thousands of acres of barren Afghan steppelands will perhaps become flourishing farms, and this sturdy race will have considerably more to eat. Give an Afghan meat and spinach, and the world may well see a stand for independence that will defy penetration from other quarters. For these people dislike invasion. They learned after losing to Alexander, Genghis Khan, Tamerlane, and each other. And they've done some pretty fancy penetrating themselves. They are the fellows who surged down out of their plateau and set up their kings to be India's rugged line of Grand Moguls.

How Morrison-Knudsen got into this upland country and what it's doing there is part of the current flow of history. It underscores the role of America's many unsung "ambassadors with power shovels" who are doing a great international job of friendship-building for the U.S.A. And it gives point to the quiet work being done by such chaps as M-K's agronomist, Dr. Claude L. Fly, who is showing that the Afghan's average per capita diet of 1,600 calories a day not only should be doubled but can be through proper use of the land.

The country lies in a triangle formed by two rivers of Asia, the Oxus and the Indus, with a backbone of rock and cliff. There's not a foot of railroad in its 270,000 square miles. There are no navigable waterways. It's as landlocked as Switzerland, but unlike that busy nation, which knows so much about time that it makes the world's watches and clocks, Afghanistan doesn't know time at all. The land has eight to a dozen million people. For the bulk of them the most technical thing in their experience is still a donkey or a camel, and a wheelbarrow is a mechanical marvel. When M-K moved in, a man would walk straight up against a moving truck, never dreaming that its speed and weight would bowl him over; a piece of whirring machinery was something to arouse curiosity, even at the immediate loss of a hand or finger.

In 1944 the Afghan ruler decided to do something about the food supply. He instructed his minister in Washington to ask the U.S. to send a consulting engineer and appropriate advice. The consultant was Dr. J. L. Savage—the Colonel Jack Savage who, as chief engineer of the Reclamation Service, had bossed the designing of Hoover Dam and of innumerable U.S. works before and since. Savage recommended repairs to existing irrigation dams and an extension of the Boghra Canal, an important work which was then being excavated by primitive methods under Japanese supervision. For detailed planning and construction, Colonel Savage suggested Morrison-Knudsen, of Boise and San Francisco.

Boise is almost exactly 180 degrees of longitude from Afghanistan's capital of Kabul, so the two points couldn't be farther from each other. You can look up Broadway or down Warm Springs Avenue in Boise and never see a camel or a veiled woman, a mosque, a minaret, or a turban. But you can't look down a Boise street without seeing a Morrison-Knudsen man who has probably just come from Brazil or New Zealand and is on his way to Morocco or Labrador. And down in San Francisco was Charley Dunn, vice-president of M-K in charge of overseas operations and head of M-K's International Engineering Company. Dunn is a plum-shaped man whose lips around a comfortable old pipestem continually shape themselves into a reminiscent grin. The chuckle follows, burbling like the mess in his pipe. His eyes twinkle even when he is examining an expense account. His knowledge of earth and men extends over a span about equal to H. W. Morrison's.

Word of Mohammed Zahir Shah's interest in irrigation reached this diligent earth changer. He buzzed for his secretary and told her to set out the suitcase packed with ten shirts that always stands in the office closet, and he was on his way to Kabul. The journey came in nicely: there was also a dam in prospect on the Yangtse, and another in Ceylon, and anyway he'd been home at least a week and a man gets restless.

Dunn made the trip from Peshawar to the Afghan border by train. His supplies were some cans of sardines, a chunk of cheese, some beer, and a tin of Brindley's smoking mixture. He entered by Khyber Pass. Until his coming, probably not more than a hundred Americans had ever been in Afghanistan.

The caravans that come down through Khyber and the other passes of Afghanistan are out of another age. Sometimes they contain thousands of pack animals, and anybody going in the reverse direction had better get off the trail. The coming and going includes men trudging with back-packs, wearily pushing up and over the mountains in gondola-shaped shoes; women sheathed to the eyes, riding the tough native horses; gypsylike nomads, their women gaily dressed and unveiled; camels, herds of sheep and goats, and great dogs. To Pakistan go dried and fresh fruits, rugs, karakul skins, grain, silk, hair and wool. Back come sugar, cotton piece goods, radio sets and parts for the kingdom's few busses and trucks. Kabul is in the eastern end of the kingdom. Kandahar, the second major town, is 320 miles southwest.

Waves of invasion have mixed up the population and made it rough and hardy. Tribe feuds with tribe and family with family like outraged Kentucky mountaineers, and raids and roughhousings keep the local politics churned. The passes are studded with stone lookout huts and citadels. Hawk-faced riflemen like to range the hills. The people are Moslems. In swales and on hillocks may be seen the occasional tents of herdsmen-nomads, who "follow the grass" from Russian steppes to far down across the borders of Baluchistan and Iran, minding their own business and making their own law. Nobody asks the nomad for his passport. If he did, it would probably be produced in the form of a poke from a rifle. After a season's camp the tents move on, leaving a new little cemetery up on a knoll; the sheep, goats, donkeys and camels and great wolfdogs and weathered herdboys vanish over the horizon; the almost nonexistent grass recovers a little; and one day new tents appear.

The present monarchy had been running the country for about two hundred years. Back in 1926 the current king's uncle visited Europe and came home with some novel ideas. He started to order the veils off the women, educate the youth, and give coeducation a whirl. But that was moving too fast. There was upheaval and assassination. For the next two decades the soft pad-pad and bubbly wheeze of the one-hump camel continued to be the dominant industrial sound in the land. But now the rulers, Mohammed Zahir Shah and his advisers, were ready to talk modernization again. And this time they were leaving the *chowdris* on the women; they were simply talking better farming and maybe electric power.

Dunn's outfit set up a unit called Morrison-Knudsen Afghanistan, Inc., and in 1946 it made a contract with the Ministry of Public Works to construct $22 million worth of dams, canals, and roads, $17,500,000 of which was to be paid for in U.S. dollars. This was to be raised by the Afghan government through the sale of karakul furs. D. J. Bleifuss, the chief engineer of M-K's International Engineering Company, buckled down to the detailed estimating and within three months the M-K people began to arrive in force.

The first undertakings were roads and irrigation matters in the vicinity of Kabul. They were not showy works, but they were sound, and the Americans, those free-striding fellows with the open-neck shirts, soon began moving dirt.

Although there were shipping strikes in the United States, embargoes on rail shipments in Pakistan, and massacres owing to the partition difficulties between Pakistan and India, M-K's equipment and material lumbered through. When pilfering in Khyber Pass threatened to rob M-K down to its undershirts, Dunn personally picked out the grimmest-looking chief in the district and, for a reasonable stipend, offered him the job of guarding the goods. The sheik, overcome by such a compliment, put armed soldiers in pairs over the matériel, and when he turned in his bill it was for exactly the wages of the six riflemen—six rupees or $1.80 a day for the lot. Nothing ever again disappeared that was under his eagle eye. "He looked like a decent citizen to me," says Dunn, "and he was proud to be trusted." Proud, and perhaps just a little surprised.

For two years dirt flew in eastern Afghanistan. Meanwhile soil surveys and economic studies showed a pressing need for development work about 300 miles southwest. The soil was rich, yet the majority of the people were barely existing. To put it in comparative figures: the average U.S. citizen received $1,400 in 1955, of which he spent 29 per cent for food and drew down in return a daily 3,250-calorie diet containing an array of good things—96 grams of protein, plenty of meat, and fruits, vegetables, minerals, and vitamins galore. But the average per capita income in the huge southwest section of Afghanistan was $25 for a whole year's work; only one person in five was a wage earner; to nourish himself, the worker ate *non*, the local bread, perhaps some grapes and garden sass, and (for the entire year) 15 pounds of meat. Only half the population got that much. Only 10 per cent had a sustaining diet or better, including meat, milk, and fruit. As for schooling, it was largely unheard of. The food experts decided that the region must triple its total food supply, and for health's sake should do it in the direction of more non-grain and livestock farming, together with crops that would furnish material for light manufactures. The call was for more pasture and hay for livestock; for oil-seed crops, increased fruits and nuts, and specialty crops—tobacco, hemp and other fibers; and medicinal, spice, and flavor crops.

Fortunately the land was adapted to it, provided it received water, and the water, some 5 million acre-feet a year, was there if harnessed. Southern Afghanistan is drained by the Helmand River system and a large tributary, the Arghandab, which gather their waters in the folds and foothills of the Hindu Kush. The river system has been tapped by primitive hand-dug tunnels and ditches for generations and the soil, which is deep sediment in the bottoms, has long grown field and orchard crops in the immediate vicinity of those trickles. A few feet away all is desert. The Helmand empties into shallow lakes in the southwestern corner of the country, along the Iranian border. In past ages the rivers discharging into this inland sea carried large quantities of sediment. With change of climate the sea receded, exposing a broad flat terrain of deep silt. The portion of this region which lies in Afghanistan is known as the Chakansur. It has been cultivated to a greater or lesser extent since the dawn of history. A traveler still kicks up old coins dating back to Tiglath Pileser of Assyria, Cyrus of Persia, and the Romans. This region suffers from a rough climate, however, for the normal rainfall is very low, and a hot, strong wind blows continuously during the 120 days of summer.

The raging torrents of Helmand Valley's spring floods for ages have sent millions of acre-feet of water charging southward to the Chakansur, to be wasted in the inland seas of Afghanistan and Iran. Dams and reservoirs were obviously needed. Kajakai and Arghandab reservoirs were to be preludes to a new sort of life in the parched but potentially fertile region. The work was launched of harnessing the Hel-

mand and Arghandab rivers and pushing canals out into
800,000 thirsty acres of bottom, bench, and desert.

The job was an extraordinary problem of logistics and of
human relations. Equipment being hard to come by because
of those shortages at home, Harry Olson, Norman Kelly, and
other executives and mechanical experts of M-K went out to
Saipan in the Pacific and bought the trucks and other heavy
stuff that had been left there at the end of the war. If the
equipment was serviceable it was loaded on a ship and sent
to Portland, Oregon, where M-K set up a big repair shop; and
then to Pakistan for the long trip up and over Khyber or
Kojak Pass. Southwestern Afghanistan was so far out of the
ordinary travel routes that it had no roads except donkey
trails when M-K came in; its grim Kojak Pass at the Baluchistan border is still closed down by the Pakistan soldiery
daily at 5 P.M. because, beyond the British-built railhead at
Chaman, the rugged hills are brigand and kidnap country.
Mud-walled forts erected as caravansaries by recent mon-
archs attest that the plundering of travelers is a recognized way of making a living. That habit has only lately been
knocked out of business—by the 80-mile hard highway for
fast-moving motor vehicles which M-K has brought to the
land. At Kandahar, the metropolis of the Helmand-Arghan-
dab which Afghans say has 50,000 people (women are not
counted in the census), it is sometimes impossible even to
mail a letter, for the shah's post office may be out of stamps.
In this ancient city, which dates beyond the conquering
Alexander whose name it wears, no women's faces are to be
seen beneath the heavy cloths that shelter those uncomforta-
ble creatures head to heels. If a man owns a chicken, he ties
it by a leg-string close to his doorstep; if he has an enemy who
has killed one of his kin, the law permits him to personally

remove the head of the offender in the market place; if he owns an overcoat, he wears it though the temperature be over 100 degrees, and his job a pick-and-shovel one—for to put his coat down would be to invite prompt robbery; if a husband at any time desires a divorce, he can have one in five minutes for 15 cents.

The railroad from the Indus plains up to Quetta, last city of size in Pakistan, is one of the steepest standard-gauge lines in operation anywhere, and its down trips are safeguarded by derailing switches designed to direct a runaway train more or less harmlessly up hill. Cars are nineteenth-century, wooden affairs and sieves for dust; passengers carry their own bedrolls and water and spend the twenty-two hours between Karachi and the border in freeze or swelter. At lofty Quetta, a town which lost 30,000 souls some years ago by earthquake, a government road leads over the pass to Chaman, the last Pakistani outpost. Beyond, the only roads are what Morrison-Knudsen laid down to serve construction needs. It took 50,000 different items, all imported from afar, to put water behind Helmand and Arghandab damsites, and most of those items came over Kojak Pass. Four customs and passport stations stand in the way beyond that point and the M-K drivers still may not go through without rigid inspections and fresh visas. Their passport books grow to have so many extra pages of visas that they look like accordions. The construction firm put F. H. James down at Karachi to get goods and personnel across the docks and through Pakistan's formalities, and Ed Sage up at Chaman on the extreme border. And stuff and men, and some wives too, began arriving. It takes canny judgment, understanding of men, and monumental patience to get matériel and men through a seaport and country which are as unfriendly to their ultimate destination as Pakistan is to Afghanistan. In later years this tough chore has fallen to Dick Fuller, who in the war went from Wake to a Jap prison camp and there acquired, by great suffering, the patience his Karachi job needed. Patience with speed. Fuller somehow managed to get the two into double harness.

Magnus Erlander, Olof and Tooe's third son, saw an ad in the papers for mechanics overseas and presented himself to M-K-A. He was sent at once to Karachi. There he scarcely had time to stare at his first camel when he was given command of trucks to take across the Sind desert and up over the high Baluchistan hills for Kandahar. The journey, he was told, ought to take two or three days. He was briefed on the route, given a map, supplied with water and grub, and he set out. The month was June. The Indus plains were green. People waved as the trucks, loaded with crated tractors and shovels, trundled by.

The country began to tilt up. Greenery disappeared. All was rock, swept bare as by a broom. Wind whistled down the gullies and it was harsh and dry—out of Inner Asia by way of the passes and bleak high slopes of the Hindu Kush. On the fourth morning they ground their way up and over the windings of Kojak Pass. Several thousand feet below, the southwestern Afghan desert shimmered in the morning sun. Dust eddies, or "go-devils," whirled over its gravelly surface like dancers. Tall dark mountains lifted, some of them covered to the knees or higher by advancing dunes. Off to the south a complete waste, the Desert of Death, lay behind a long white bluff that suggested the combers of the sea.

But Magnus also beheld, down on the vacant flat, the long straight line of that M-K highway, leading straight to Kandahar. Eighty miles more and, close to Kandahar's mud walls and huts, he came to the rectangle or compound of Manzil Bagh, Garden of Rest for the Traveler and summer palace of the king, which Morrison-Knudsen had leased for its construction camp. Magnus delivered his cargoes to a building that had been the royal harem, now a storehouse for tractor parts, and stamped into the messhall for a man-sized breakfast.

Engineers and technicians and their wives in the vicinity of Kandahar soon had a flourishing little Suburbia right in the middle of the land of ancient aqueducts and bazaars. Well-furnished barracks went up for the single men. Machine shops and drafting rooms began to sprout. Into the compound the equipment came rolling. The machines were examined with voluble interest by the camel drivers, muleteers, crag-hopping riflemen, and oriental rug weavers who, 3,500 in all, were being trained to become the operators of everything from Monighan draglines and Euclid trucks down to No. 2 mucksticks.

First came diversion structures and a great cleaning out and extending of old canals. In April of 1950 the government entered into a contract for additional construction, and negotiated a loan with the Export-Import Bank for $21 million. The new contract provided for the construction of a dam on the Helmand near Kajakai village, a dam on the Arghandab River, the principal tributary of the Helmand, and extension of the main or Boghra Canal some 35 kilometers farther, together with a big branch canal to follow the flood plain of the Helmand some 65 kilometers.

Kajakai Dam, an earth and rock structure, was built at a point in Helmand Canyon where the river cut a narrow slot through a limestone ridge. Just above this point the valley widens into a broad plain. The site was an engineer's dream—a very short dam would impound 3 million acre-feet.

After a period of engineering studies and layouts, and a year spent gathering equipment from half around the world, scalers went to work on the canyon's rock-wall abutments with jackhammer and broom, with two big tunnels to be carved and the river diverted, and construction of the dam to begin in the summer of 1951.

The tunnels were no playthings. A pair of horseshoe-shaped holes each 35 feet wide and half a mile long, they took digging, and the task was performed by Afghans who up to that time had never been deeper into the earth than a furrow excavated by a wooden plow, or a molelike irrigation burrow. One tunnel would later be used to carry water for irrigation and the other for power production in a future hydroelectric plant. The man in charge of the tunnel work under dam builder Jim Dunn was Lowell C. (Blackie) Thomas, who arrived in the land of the fat-tailed sheep after driving the Union Pacific's Altamont tunnel in Wyoming and some spectacular bores in Alaska. Along with turning the Helmand, Blackie also turned the Arghandab—and many an itchy-fingered tribesman, instead of potshooting his neighbors, learned the fun and excitement of setting off a bunch of giant powder with an electric plunger and watching an acre of limestone quiver, bulge, and collapse. And there Kajakai Dam stands today, 320 feet high from bedrock and 1,017 feet along its crest, and the big lake it creates brings the nomads from afar to stare at, dip toe in, and still disbelieve.

The Arghandab Valley project comprised a separate agricultural entity within the Helmand watershed. Arghandab Dam, a rolled earth-fill structure, was started in 1950 and completed in early 1952 ahead of schedule, and a sight it is—

a plug rising 194 feet to a crest 1,740 feet long, backing up a lake of about 385,000 acre-feet of life-giving water, which pours out through a house-high tunnel 866 feet long.

The two structures, striking though they are, stand in their rugged hills unglimpsed by anyone save the occasional no-mad or the determined traveler who bumps by jeep over the now untended construction roads for scores of miles. But out on the far-lying plains new homes are rising, new villages, and new hopes.

To be the on-the-ground boss of the whole project, after a succession of managers, came T. Y. Johnston, "Mr. M-K-A of the U.S.A." More than a construction man, he is a first-rate builder of good will between peoples—which is exactly Harry Morrison's idea everywhere.

Manager Johnston realized, at the conclusion of the work authorized under the first Export-Import Bank loan, that cer-tain light construction necessary to the next phase of develop-ment could be economically performed by an organization of Afghan nationals. This organization, supervised and con-trolled by the Afghan government's Helmand Valley Author-ity, would be staffed with American key personnel for the time being, with Afghan understudies. When the under-studies became proficient, they would take over management and operations of the appropriate jobs. This Afghan Con-struction Unit is currently in operation in several areas. All items of secondary construction, such as interception drains, on-the-farm drainage, land leveling, farm ditches, and prep-aration of land for seeding, together with the beginnings of afforestation, are being done by the Afghan Construction Unit. These forces will continue with the work as M-K-A fin-ishes its contracts.

In 1954 the Export-Import Bank approved a loan for another $18,500,000, in U.S. dollars, calling for electric power, further irrigation works, and the erection and settlement of a brand-new city and agricultural area called Marja, far down-valley. An able Em-Kayan named Otto Oetjen is the area superintendent and "mayor" of that 30,000-acre region and he is having the time of his life converting sand to spinach and Bedouins to farmers.

There is much more yet to be done—farms ditched and drained, salts leached out, and the new green land divided among the nomadic people—though this last is the king's worry, not M-K's.

What will it all mean for the common man of Afghanistan? That is a question with a hundred answers. Farming in settled style means, for the nomad, giving up the roaming way of life with all its freedoms; means vulnerability to the tax collector; means obedience to king's law instead of tribal law; looks to him like a caging up and a shackling. To date, many of the tribesmen tarry only where the water flows cost-free, far beyond the limits of the king's project. There they grow a crop and move on. How long does it take to anchor down a free-rover, make him build a permanent shelter, and teach him new ways?

Yet solid achievements have come out of it. M-K's technicians and foremen have taught thousands of people new trades. They have built several hundred miles of roads, over an area as big as the state of Iowa, and those roads will endure for public travel for a number of years to come. At Kandahar, in the construction camp compound, the construction men have built and equipped one perfect little 15-bed hospital complete with everything a modern physician or surgeon could ask for. It's for anybody who needs medical help, whether an M-K employee or not. Unfortunately few

Afghans understand how to use it. A man with a broken leg will crawl out of bed before he is released and creep home as fast as possible to keep his clothes from being stolen. And a woman who needs hospital help would rather die than let a strange man see her or a stethoscope touch her. Ted Johnston's model hospital, M-K's gift to the Afghan people, is one little candle flickering in the dark. Perhaps its flame will not go out. Perhaps it will even kindle others, and radiate new concepts of sanitation and hygiene in a land of mud huts, ignorance, and flies.

But the old ways die hard.

Meanwhile the Soviet Union, from the north, digs with lusty spadework at the barrier which the West is trying to strengthen—the bulwark of a manly, freedom-loving people badly in need of food and economic hope.

12

RUBBING ALADDIN'S OILY LAMP

THE SHORES which slope back from the Persian Gulf
are estimated to contain three-quarters of the world's oil. Of
this, the concession in Saudi Arabia held by Arabian-American Oil Company—Aramco—has proved reserves of 35 billion
barrels.

A two-hour drive takes you over more oil than is believed
to underlie the whole U.S.A. In the proved area, when a well
is wanted, a hole is punched; the result is of the free-flowing
order of 10,000 barrels a day.

And the proved area is constantly widening. Perhaps it extends straight up to Kuwait. Even in the early years of
Aramco, the local monarch must have been amazed at his
lucky partnership.

The career of this ruler had been one of extreme hardship.
A son of the king of the Nejd, as the coastless inner core of
Araby is called, he had been expelled from his native Riyadh
in a palace upheaval and had spent his early years with the
nomads, scrabbling for a handful of dates and a crust.

At the turn of the century he was a raw-boned youth who
had been on the lam most of his life. But he was a strapper

with a great sword-arm, and one night he struck back for his patrimony and a good slice more. He went over Riyadh's wall with seven followers, lay low until dawn, clove and hacked his way to the usurper, hauled that worthy through a doorway by one leg, saw him dispatched, and flung open the town gates to thirty more followers. The people rose and made him king of Riyadh and the Nejd. Because he had become a Bedouin of the Bedouins, tribesmen flocked to him; in three decades he was master of Arabia from Persian Gulf to Red Sea and from the great Empty Quarter in the southeast almost to Damascus and River Jordan in the north.

He was lord and warden of the holy cities of Mecca and Medina and the commercial port of Jiddah. He operated this stretch from high-walled Riyadh, and Riyadh itself was as hard for a foreigner to enter as Mecca, Lhassa, or the moon, and he kept it that way. In fact, he and the tribesmen kept the whole Nejd that way. But he was a monarch of a land that was all gravel and dunes and poverty. A lord only of valiant people and a lot of space.

Then, as he was tightening his grip on this austere realm, something happened over on the gulf shore. This was the landing of a little group of American geologists from Bahrain, a nearby island where Standard of California had hit oil in a big way.

The geologists wanted to look around. They managed to obtain audience with this lord of middle Araby who was famous for his towering height, his sword, his lusty humor, his faculty for large-scale fatherhood, his bare royal cupboard and his empty treasury. The geologists offered the king a sizable share in any wealth they might find.

The tall king pondered. He consulted his doctors of Islamic law. He let the Americans explore. And what they found turned out to be one-sixth of the known reserves of all the oil on earth. Standard of California invited other companies in on the development and in a couple of decades production was up to a million barrels a day. Qatar and Abqaiq fields were famous.

So the man who had spent years in the saddle, lashing about in search of his next meal, found himself riding in motorcars that grew longer and longer and went faster and faster; sampling movies, radio, refrigerators, air conditioning. Life became wonderful and he had the gusto for it. But he remained every inch the king. He considered all things in terms of their impact on his people. Some gadgets were excellent but others were clearly against Islamic custom. He did allow radios and motor vehicles to be brought in. Gradually Bedouin tents began to sprout aerials, and here and there a pickup truck appeared, or at least a donkey cart with pneumatic tires.

Because oil was all over the Persian Gulf country and oil meant pipelines and refineries, American constructors were all over the gulf country too, including Bechtel forces. The king learned from Aramco, his oil partners, that those men could do anything, and do it quickly.

His spending money was beginning to bother him. He decided he'd like to own a small electric power plant. He called in Bill O'Neill, a Bechtel electrical engineer, and told him to get busy. Bill put the plant in, and for some time it was used solely to operate an X-ray machine. The king had all four wives, uncounted spares, forty sons, and visiting sheiks X-rayed; the resulting portraits of hidden skeletons and other in'ards delighted him.

The notion of lighting the apartments and grounds of the old palace came later. When it came, it did so with a rush.

Bill was directed to wire the gardens for a dinner for five hundred and to make things brilliant. Time at Bill's disposal, seventeen days. At this stage there was not a powerhouse or a suitable generator within 350 miles. By radio and plane the urgent messages went out and the stuff came in, flown from New York. When the dinner party was held, there were the lights in dazzling quantity all through the date palms.

As oil flowed out, and revenues gushed in, His Majesty discovered that he wanted a new palace. The image of it came to him, full blown, one night in a dream.

He summoned an Arab contractor for that one. It was to be a rose-red palace that would cost exactly one million dollars, no more, no less, and it was to look exactly so and so and it was to stand right here. The foundations were to start immediately; don't stall around over drawings and specifications. So, just outside Riyadh's medieval walls, the Red Palace rose to its several stories, with bays and arched windows and colonnades and cupolas, and a compound wall, an impressive gate, and a formal garden with colored fountains. When the neon lights were turned on, the sumptuous building sprang forth on the Arabian desert like something out of Monte Carlo by way of Coney Island, finished off in pink whipped cream by a Viennese pastry cook.

Ibn Saud didn't live to occupy his dreamboat. But his successor son, the present King Saud, moved in while far vaster palaces of his own were going up. In '56 the writer of these lines stepped over the grounded rifles of guardsmen at the gate, was permitted to walk the length of seemingly endless red carpet, advanced up the steps into the many-mirrored palace, and had coffee with the king. The great salon where levees are held is a carpeted apartment walled with mirrors at the bases of which, ranging the room on four sides, are a hundred or so chairs of French gilt. These are occupied by robed sheiks who have come to pay their respects, and they ride the graceful pieces of furniture as assuredly as ever they sat a horse. King Saud, tall like his father and a man of singular dignity and courtesy, with a light smile ever playing on his lips, occupies a similar chair but it is covered by a leopard skin. Night and day the electrified chandeliers blaze like Times Square at show time. Floyd Ohliger, director and vice-president of Aramco, was conductor and mentor for this visitor, and had cautioned him to hold the coffee cup in the right hand, never in the left; to leave as soon as the frankincense had been passed; and similar amenities. All of which he did. To find, upon his return to his night's sleeping quarters, the gold *agal*, headcloth and robes of an honorary Arab sheik. But, fortunately, no riding camel.

Riyadh today is like no other city in the world. In its leap from camel to airplane, it is at once primitive and fabulous, poverty-ridden and opulent, like a barefooted Bedouin wading through diamonds. The airport, which knows virtually only Aramco's and the king's own planes, has a waiting room floored in rugs of price, every chair almost a throne for upholstery and size, and coffee served the instant one sits down. Emirs and sheiks abound, and everyone shakes hands with a Montana grip. Araby's flies cling to one's mouth, nose, and eyes and practically have to be grabbed by a leg and thrown off. Yet it is stated that DDT has reduced their former number by fully 99 per cent.

Outside of town the tracks of immemorial camel caravans lie deep, but in the city automobiles are beginning to be a nuisance even as in the Chicago Loop or Picadilly Circus. Traffic, however, is better controlled. When fatalities began to occur, the king simply announced that any driver who caused a death would be beheaded.

The writer was in Riyadh just in time to see the last of the medieval houses and garden walls disappear before the bulldozer. Dust and chaos were complete. A short while before, only one house in this town of 60,000 people had been built of anything but sun-dried mud. But what was going on was a complete demolition and replacement job—everything to be new and fine, of masonry and concrete. And outside the town a French drilling outfit was down 4,000 feet looking for water, praying that water would be found, not oil. Since then, somewhat deeper, the water was hit and the new Riyadh may now have a drink that hasn't been dipped out of a shallow hole with a goatskin. At sight of the homes, stores, schools, and hospitals rising and the wide streets being hacked through the debris, together with the complex of palaces with three main buildings (one for the ladies), a couple hundred villas, and a thousand-car garage, all inside a new 5-mile wall, the visitor asked, "Would it be ridiculous to say a hundred million is being spent here?"

"Yes, it would be ridiculous," he was informed by the construction man who was tooling him around. "The figure is nearer two hundred million."

The building boom which had hit Riyadh, hundreds of miles out in the middle of the Nejd, had hit other Arab points, too. Jiddah on the Red Sea was in a roar of rebuilding. Mecca may be, for all that a non-Moslem can guess. Morrison-Knudsen lately took up a contract to rebuild the railroad from Damascus to Jiddah which T. E. Lawrence blew up in World War I. On the Persian Gulf the rivalry of Dammam and Al Khobar is like that of Dallas and Fort Worth. New buildings are being pulled down before they are finished to make room

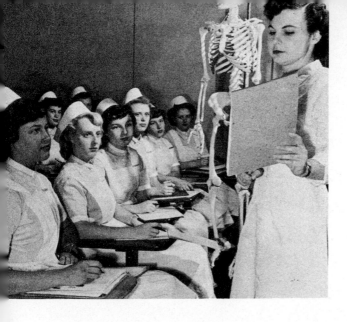

Kaiser Foundation takes three years to train nurses. Below, a modern maternity room at a Kaiser Foundation Hospital.

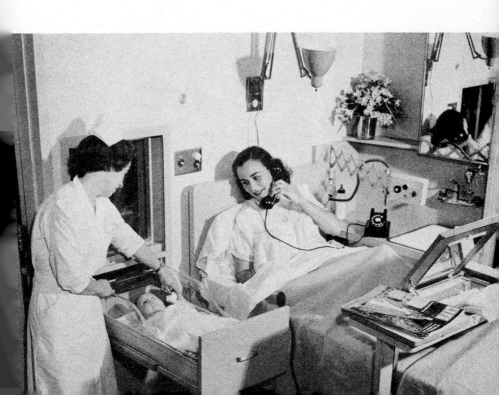

Drafting and designing employ hundreds at Kaiser home office.

Allen D. Christensen in the field at Pima Mine, Arizona.

Big Eildon Dam captures a river in Australia.

Utah Construction helped turn a San Francisco square into a four-story underground garage, while below a Utah-built canal carries Columbia water to the desert.

A 25-foot concrete pipe a mile long, Grand Coulee country.

Base camp at Alcan's river-through-a-mountain project.

Concreting main bore under Mount DuBose, British Columbia.

for others still newer and taller. Al Khobar even has a traffic light. A few years ago these were fishing villages.

The royal take from the concession to Aramco, $6 million in 1941, was $272 million in 1955 and it isn't diminishing. The present king, generous to a fault, showers gifts everywhere— one Swiss factory received a single order for 4,500 gold watches—and report has it that when he flew to Iran to visit the shah, it took one DC-3 plane to carry the presents, one of them a $900,000 necklace for the queen. While in Iran he dropped in with his retinue on a Morrison-Knudsen construction camp at the Karadj damsite, enjoyed a construction stiff's hearty lunch, and passed out a certified wrist chronometer worth close to $1,000 to the camp steward. He also dropped a lesser watch and a month's pay into the hand of each waiter. His trip to the U.S.A. as President Eisenhower's guest in 1957 did not diminish the legend of gift-strewing. However, the oil money isn't all going out in this form. Schools and hospitals and roads are also beginning to appear in Saudi Arabia. A few years ago only one motor vehicle in five was Arab-owned; the rest were Aramco's. Today, with traffic greatly multiplied, four motor vehicles out of five belong to Arabs, and many of these were penniless tribesmen only yesterday. Great is oil! Aladdin had his wonderful lamp and he got whatever he wanted by rubbing it. King Saud has picked up the lamp from Ibn Saud's hands. He enjoys royalties approaching $300 million a year and Saudi Arabia will never again be quite the same. Not by a 35-billion-barrel jugful. What the end will be, Allah knows. And He has not released His intentions through any prophet.

13

A RAILROAD FOR THE KING

THE strong-minded gentleman wanted a railroad. Other people have wanted railroads too, or swimming pools or a castle in Spain or a hundred million dollars or just a day off; but the gentleman who wanted this railroad was different. What he wanted he usually got.

'Abd al-Aziz ibn 'Abd al-Rahman Al Faisal Al Sa'ud, the King of Saudi Arabia (father of the present King Saud), by the middle 1940s was drawing millions a year from the oil beneath his feet. His Cadillacs were fast, his way with a buck still faster, and his temper when aroused was the swiftest thing of all. And he did want a railroad. From his inland capital to a port on the Persian Gulf. Now!

Word was conveyed to three American construction outfits currently active in the Middle East. They were Bechtel International Corporation, Morrison-Knudsen International Company, and Sverdrup & Parcel. And they sent a worthy team to make a study. There were enough high-powered engineers dispatched for that reconnaissance to have built a railroad from Alaska to Cape Horn, with the Trans-Siberia for a feeder. Carl M. Ney was there, retired chief engineer of the

Great Northern Railway; Dr. Laurence I. Hewes, chief of western headquarters, U. S. Public Roads Administration; and Donald L. Roberts of Bechtel, Emerson B. Steele of Morrison-Knudsen, and Percy Z. Michener of Sverdrup & Parcel. Earl F. English, then Bechtel's international trouble shooter, was chairman of the group. They left San Francisco late in 1946 and traveled from New York to Jiddah, where they were met by the king's airplane and whisked to the other side of Arabia.

From the plane they looked down upon a wrinkled land of red sands and dry washes. An ancient, a fabulous land, poor in certain of the world's goods just now; but with all this oil gushing out, who could say what days were ahead?

Landed at Dhahran, headquarters of Arabian-American Oil Company, they toured the core of Islam by sandmobile and plane, and laid out His Majesty's line.

Two-thirds of the seven or eight million people of Saudi Arabia live near the Red Sea, but there are a million along the Persian Gulf and another million and a half in the inland province of Nejd. Riyadh, the capital, had for centuries drawn its scanty imports from the two coasts by the long haul via camel, or more latterly by trucks over a road that was merely a scratch on the ground.

The consultants estimated the potential freight for the king's railroad at 400 tons a day, and decided that the iron road would haul 50,000 people a year. For the king himself is a tourist attraction to his people. Arabs love to view him, to recount their woes, and to receive his presents. Yes, a railroad would be a big help to that kind of traffic. Being true engineers, the consultants sweated out a report. They observed that ". . . the dress of the people in the cities indicates the need of a much larger supply of clothing and yardage goods. Also, there are very few modern household appliances. One obvious reason is the lack of power and fuel for operation of appliances. With oil available for the production of electric power and heating, many items such as electric refrigerators, air conditioning units, electric fans and heating units will be marketable." They added, "Saudi Arabia has one resource which is most important and which eventually will overcome any possible deficiencies—the steadfast determination of His Majesty the King to provide for his people."

There was also a compliment to the topography of the land. "The route selected follows one of the oldest camel trails between Hofuf and Riyadh—the Musaliq Trail. The ability of the operators of ancient caravans to work out such a direct and useful line of travel is unanimously recognized by the consultants as worthy of mention in this report." It cost $30 a ton to carry freight between Riyadh and the sea by camel but they decided that a railroad could do it for $8.73. And they added the finest piece of news that had been heard in the ancient peninsula since Moses smote the rock: "It will be necessary to provide additional water supplies by drilling wells along the route . . . Geologists . . . estimate that water can be found anywhere along the selected route at depths not exceeding 600 feet."

One last duty the consultants felt honor-bound to perform. They had to tell the king that he could build a trucking highway more cheaply than his railroad. But they hastened to add that if His Majesty really wanted a railroad, he could certainly have it.

Well, His Majesty really wanted it, and why the hell the delay? The king wanted a railroad even more than he wanted a repo t.

So the line came into being.

The Saudi Arabian Government iron road starts at Dammam on the gulf and it terminates at Riyadh. The road's single standard-gauge track runs through sand dunes, gravel bluffs, and temperatures of from 110 degrees up. The American contractors built it to Hofuf, a halfway point which is a trading town and an oasis, with a veteran railroader named James Gildea supervising its construction for the government. Jim himself finished the line for the government with Arab help, and he has stayed on as its general manager. He is a thin-haired, gray-eyed, quiet-voiced man with a thoughtful manner and deep human understanding, who started his railroading as a call boy on the Union Pacific in Wyoming. He rose through all the usual grades until he was assistant superintendent on the tough blustery stretch between Cheyenne and Ogden—right over the Rockies. In 1941 he joined the Army and ran military railways in Iran, India, and Europe. Next he was U.S. member of an allied transportation board in Europe. About the time he was considering a return to Cheyenne, he was tapped for supervising the Saudi Arabian railroad-building chore.

With Bechtel constructors committed to do the port work and the first couple hundred miles of main line, work started. "This is a hell of a place to build a railroad," commented Jim. A causeway and trestle had to be run out into the Persian Gulf 7 miles to find water deep enough for ships. Practically everything—ties, rails, rolling stock, handling equipment— had to come by ship. The ties cost $5.10 apiece to import and lay. For 356 miles the line pushed out into the desert. The toughest job was beating that desert sand. The stuff drifted, it blew, it marched. In two windy hours it could cover the rails 6 inches deep. It was licked when grading equipment leveled it off on the windward side of the tracks and good gooey crude oil was doused on it. Flash floods also caused plenty of trouble. Three hundred culverts finally took care of the usually dry but sometimes raging wadies.

It was a routine job for the American joint venturers, routine because everything happened which could happen to make men swear and sweat. A bulldozer sank in the ooze of a salt bed which had looked dry enough to rear a skyscraper on. Surveyor's stakes and wooden trestles disappeared into Bedouin cook fires. When the first engine arrived, crated and dismantled, and was being put together, a swirling sandstorm came up from nowhere and all but buried the camp. The region was guaranteed to provide not more than 3 inches of rain a year, but it produced that quota all at once, caught it up swiftly into the hot sky and dropped it again and again. Same 3 inches, swore the local sheiks and emirs, just the same three, bouncing up and down.

Other problems developed. When it turned out to be against the customs of one of the religious sects for a good Moslem to touch grease or clean up tools, some less particular Moslems had to be rounded up and trained to do that. When a foreman gave orders, his Arab workman invariably accepted with the word, *Inshallah,* meaning "if God wills." Very exasperating to a foreman.

When causeway and docks were constructed, rails laid, warehouses built, and a cannon boomed to welcome its first ship, the arriving freighter steamed straight for the pierhead and split it like a melon. The Scandinavian skipper tried to explain that the sun got in his eyes or a mirage or something, but the Arabs rejoiced at the excitement. It was a great day.

This is no slapdash railroad. Its roadbed is one that any train in America would be proud to run over. It cost $62 million to build, and took four years. Six hundred Arabs turned

gandy dancers to build it. Then thirty-two Palestinian Arabs
came over to help train Saudi Arabs in the operational details. The local people, after three months' instruction, were
first-rate engine drivers, firemen, conductors, station masters,
and mechanics. They've run the trains ever since. With two
passenger trains a day each way, there isn't much of a col-
lision problem. The trains stop three times an eight-hour day,
wherever they may be, for prayers.

For Jim Gildea this is the model railroad that every railroader dreams of building and operating. Its freight cars run
on roller bearings. It was the first railroad in either hemisphere
to install radio telephones for use between engineers of trains.
Its self-propelled Budd cars for first-class travel have wide
windows that are kept clean, and coffee is served with the
compliments of the king. The cars have breathing tubes that
stick 15 feet into the air to get above the dust. For the ordinary tribesmen and villagers who want to try rail travel
there are twenty-five reconstructed passenger coaches that
used to lurch between New York and Boston on the New
Haven line. They are painted a pretty green with the king's
coat-of-arms—crossed swords and a palm tree—for ornament;
their former passengers in and out of Grand Central Station
would hardly know them. As the Bedouins carry guns and
dirks as freely as the coaches' old NYNH&H passengers used
to carry fountain pens and brief cases, there are soldiers stationed on every train. Women travel veiled.

The passengers at first were something of a problem. Being
oriental, they declined to take the stated price of a ticket as
the final price, and turned the stations into bedlams of hag-
gle. The king had to pass a law ordering them to honor the
fixed price. As he has life and death power, his wish was
obeyed.

A permanent factor of Arabian railroading is still the sand, which can't be kept out of bearings and moving parts. But it is comparatively harmless. The winds of ages have rolled it smooth and round.

Railroading for an absolute monarch has its difficulties. One requirement laid down upon Jim Gildea was to operate on Arab time. This is a peculiar system. The Arab day begins at sunset, which is a variable matter. After that the clock follows a routine which only an Arab knoweth, but which apparently drops out most of the hours between sunset and midnight. Then it starts counting again. By using watches with dual dials and an occult method of calculation, the railroaders somehow keep their trains to a schedule, and their anti-accident record is the nearest to perfect in railroading records anywhere. It has to be. If an engineer kills somebody, the relatives of the victim are entitled to kill him.

A few years ago found 143 Americans, 165 Italians, and 200 Palestinians working for the line. Now the operating department is all Saudi Arab save for one American and one Palestinian. The only foreigners who are left in numbers are in the shop department.

In this treeless land the green cars look really refreshing as they slide along. And the road has proved itself an economic success precisely as the Reconnaissance Report foretold. It has cut the cost of transporting things. It makes the trip in seven to eleven hours that by camel used to take two to three weeks. It hauls wheat, flour, rice, sugar, tea, air conditioners, deep freezes, generators, and cement in one direction, and hides, hair, and dates in the other.

The road handles double the freight load that had been forecast, and could double that if it had the equipment. Ownership by the king, and the king being his own biggest shipper, is one of the explanations. But that doesn't simplify Jim Gildea's job. He has to get the freight through to Riyadh whether he has cars enough or not, and to keep the crews paid and the line running whether the king pays his big freight bills on time or plain forgets them. Yet the road struggles with considerable success to handle mountains of cement and Italian marble that keep arriving. A thousand or two tons of freight a day move across the pierhead or come ashore by lighter. There are usually eight or ten ships waiting to unload. In summer, when the Persian Gulf atmosphere is heavy and humid, such waiting almost drives the crews to jumping overboard.

In spite of the fine facilities for first-class travel, visitors from the Western World are not permitted to ride the full distance to Riyadh unless by special invitation. Without that, they are sternly bounced at the halfway point. Riyadh is still a veiled lady among world capitals and its present lord and master, like his late sire, sees that it remains that way.

Ibn Saud liked his iron road so well that he made plans for extending it over the Hejaz Mountains to Mecca, Jiddah, and Medina, another 900 miles. But death came to the husband and father of the vast multiple household at Riyadh before the work could be ordered, and Jim Gildea's iron horse does not yet neigh at the black-curtained rock in Mecca.

But the way oil royalties are pouring out of the soil, it will probably get there soon.

14

TAPPING A FLOATING KINGDOM

AFTERNOON on the Arabian desert found a party of American engineers far from a water hole. They had a tank on a trailer and they went into camp. Before long they discovered that they were not alone. Not by several hundred people and thousands of horses, camels, sheep, and goats. The livestock kept coming over the low hills. A pavilion arose, evidently the evening quarters of some important chieftain.

The Americans were aware that Arab tribesmen are jealous about who camps in their bailiwicks. Politeness suggested paying a call before the sheik and his armed men paid one of their own. George Colley and a companion went over. The companion knew some Arabic. With his best bow, George inquired if he might offer the sheik a drink from his water tank. For this courteous gesture George and pal were welcomed and soon found themselves cross-legged on the rug, sipping coffee. By the size of the armed retinue they knew they had encountered a powerful chief indeed. During the coffee-sipping and the silences which went with it, George hazarded the information that he was a friend of King Ibn Saud.

The sheik's sunbaked countenance turned flintlike. After an

interval for word-choosing, "I," pronounced the sheik wither-
ingly, "am an Arab who has always been an Arab. Ibn Saud is
an Arab who became an Arab."

Later George solved the riddle of this haughty remark. The
man he had met in the desert came of a local lineage that
traced back three or four thousand years. Ibn Saud's people,
only a thousand or so years ago, had come to this part of
Arabia from Damascus. In the sheik's book that made Ibn
Saud a Johnny-come-lately. Time, George perceived, is measured by millennia in the East.

Bechtel people had been at work in this part of the globe
since 1943. The first job had been a batch of refinery projects
for Bahrain Petroleum Co.—Bapco—on the little oil-soaked
island of Bahrain just off the coast. An underwater pipeline
from the mainland followed. A 50,000 barrel-a-day refinery
for Aramco at Ras Tanura on the mainland was next. Postwar
needs shoved this capacity up to 100,000 barrels in '46; 200,-
000 by 1956. By the end of the 1940s, Bechtel had helped
build a whole city at Dhahran, Aramco's headquarters. It was
only a step in the parade of towns, refineries, ports, and pipelines Bechtel put up for this client. Between 1944 and 1948
they totaled around $200 million worth.

Then came Tapline.

In 1945 the owners of Aramco started planning a pipe that
would take the Arabian peninsula at a bound and bring oil
to the shore of the Mediterranean. The line would eliminate
the twenty-day, 7,000-mile round trip by tankers down the
Persian Gulf, through the Indian Ocean to the Red Sea, and
through Suez Canal with its toll of 12 to 13 cents a barrel.
Thus was organized Trans-Arabian Pipe Line Company—
Tapline for short.

Burt E. Hull went in as Tapline's headman. Back in America, Hull had built the Big Inch and Little Inch lines during the war.

Steve Bechtel and some other figures in American construction were invited to Arabia in 1947 to discuss this pipeline. They came back with the news that International Bechtel, Inc., with associates, was going to lay the line from the Abqaiq field to beyond the Trans-Jordan border. A line almost as long as Big Inch from Texas to New York and of twice its capacity. In addition to the Tapline contract, there would be port, transportation, and other facilities built for the Saudi Arabian government. Said Steve when he got home, "In the Middle East program I foresee potentially the biggest development of natural resources ever undertaken by American interests."

When a suitable co-venturing group had been collected, old rivals and partners once more were found on an all-star team: Morrison-Knudsen Company, Inc., of Boise, Idaho; H. C. Price Co., of Bartlesville, Oklahoma; Bob Conyes of Oakland, California; Sverdrup & Parcel of St. Louis; J. H. Pomeroy & Co., Inc., of San Francisco, and the Bechtels as sponsor. They were lined up to haul, weld, and heave into place 850 miles of the 1,100-mile champion pipeline of its time. Williams Brothers Corp. of Tulsa was awarded the tough, short portion from Jordan down to Sidon. Burt Hull warned that the chief problems of the desert would be water, transport, and morale.

The portion taken over by Bechtel lay through an exceedingly empty region. A tree was as rare as a three-hump camel. Reconnaissance parties moved out into that windy void. From the Persian Gulf westward, the first hundred miles or so contained heavy sand dunes. The next 750 were wastes of gravel and rock, with occasional wadies where surface water stood or flowed after the rare showers. The route climbed to 2,975 feet near the Jordan border.

Clark Rankin and Ray Hamilton flew from San Francisco to go over the route and pick out the site for a base camp. From then on, construction men moved back and forth between America and Arabia the way commuters ride the Long Island Railroad. Van W. Rosendahl headed up the two Bechtel international corporations. Clark Rankin was put in charge of project planning. Over came George Colley, then two years out of the Kuching prison camp on Borneo where the Japs had trimmed his stocky figure to 125 pounds. He was senior Bechtel construction officer for some of the international projects. Al Berlander was construction manager. Don Roberts, who later would be project manager for Trans Mountain pipeline across Canada's Rockies, was International Bechtel's chief engineer until sand and bugs mowed him down. Bob Bowman was general superintendent, Harry Waste project engineer, and Q. Poggi in charge of transport.

Surveyors went out into the field that summer and found the temperatures, the winds, the sandstorms, and the August humidity no worse than Arizona or New Mexico in summer with perhaps a hammam bath thrown in.

Back at Dhahran the amenities of civilization, American style, had developed in a wide and handsome way. Aramco's doings in the heart of the Middle East had converted the town into the number one American community between Europe and the Philippines. It was even air-conditioned.

So Dhahran became headquarters for the contractor's principal field officers. Here IBI executive vice-president John Rogers set up shop; he was from the original refinery construction job at Ras Tanura by way of Arizona, where he'd been getting out wartime copper. Rudy Grammater, alumnus of the

Canol pipeline from the Mackenzie to the Yukon, was IBI administrative chief. Here general superintendent Lou Killian arrived in June, 1947, with nineteen American technicians. All were a picked bunch; it had cost $5,000 a head to select, process, and transport these "Camel Legionnaires." They were men who'd known and worked with each other from the Arctic Circle to South America, and now most of them started sprouting Islam-like whiskers. Lou Killian, although without the assist of a set of whiskers, is now Bechtel executive vice-president in the Middle East.

For equipment the construction forces had the benefit of the outsized equipment pool and experience of Aramco, which had been fighting local conditions for years and licking them the way Montgomery licked Rommel. As Caterpillar's best customer, Aramco stood second only to the United States Army; as a buyer of tires and special-type trucks, it knew no peer. Nothing has ever been seen on American highways like the 165-passenger personnel carriers which Aramco operates to haul its workers about; no trucker, outside of Arabia, has steered such tires as the monsters on which Aramco grinds over the dunes. With such a devotee of Bigness for a client, Bechtel's people could rejoice; and they set about developing some big stuff themselves.

There wasn't any suitable marine terminal on the Persian Gulf. So one was made.

With rangy Lou Killian in charge, camp was set up north of Dhahran on the gulf shore where some protection was afforded by a sandy hook of land that looked like a camel driver's stick. From this resemblance the place bore the name Ras al Mish'ab. The Neutral Zone which divides Saudi Arabia from oily Kuwait, at the head of the gulf, was 14 miles beyond. Lou and his party trucked up from Dhahran and staked out the camp in a howling sandstorm. The tents just did stay up.

"Our tents," recalled an old-timer, "were nicely floored with wall-to-wall sand." The occupants cussed sand, ate sand, and breathed sand along with sand flies and plain flies, the latter as thick as currants in a mince pie. Presently the mud-brick buildings of a semipermanent camp began to rise, but sand and insects remained as dependable ingredients of the atmosphere.

Soon a jetty and a pier stretched out into the blue water. Mish'ab's first cargo ship arrived two months after camp was laid out. Barges brought ashore tools and the first pipe. Unloading was a problem. Tapline borrowed an idea from the fir loggers in Oregon and Washington. At certain places in those faraway evergreen forests, loggers use overhead cables, or "skyhooks," for hauling timber from steep mountain slopes. So a skyhook was erected 3 miles out into the Persian Gulf. Twenty-four A-frames went up to hold the cable, from which self-propelled cars were hung, each capable of trundling 10 tons of pipe.

Operated in tandem, these high-wire cars made the 3-mile journey in five minutes, and presently they were bringing ashore 1,100 tons a day, swinging it along 80 feet above the water with all the fun of riding a scenic railway. Ashore, the 31-foot pipe sections were welded into triple-lengths. And soon the Abqaiq-Qatif section was in place, 24 miles of it ingeniously laid above ground on steel bents and concrete pads, held down by bolted ring girders against the winds and the curiosity of the Bedouins. The pipeliners were on their way, Gulf to Mediterranean.

For vertical alignment, the long steel pipeline was supported over the first stretches on crosspieces set on wooden piles. A machine called the "loping camel" drove these at a smart clip. Later concrete supports went in. Care was taken to weld the lengths under atmospheric temperatures as close to the mean as possible; excessively hot hours were avoided. Provision was made for camel-crossings—ramps of sand—every mile or two, unless the pipe ran under a dune or hill.

Wind blew. Sun blazed. Fahrenheits in the thermometer came down to 100 when they felt like cooling off, then struck straight up. Grit storms and rare raindrops hit like machine-gun bullets. Sand dunes shifted and slued. But men who'd built Hoover, Coulee, Pacific bases, and many "big inches" had been through a good deal of difficulty before, and knew how to hunt for the answers. To keep the truck engines cool, two radiators were used. Everything that moved got double servicing.

Long before the first black goat-hair Arab tent had been raised at Ras al Mish'ab, Ray Hamilton and his logistic experts back home had been figuring out problems to be met. Trucks and trailers too wide and too heavy for any United States highway had been built and tested on the desert of New Mexico under conditions approaching those in Saudi Arabia.

But while Ray had been able to produce trailer trucks hauling 40 tons of pipe in lengths up to 93 feet, he couldn't rid Arabia of truck-driver lonesomeness. Roads were nonexistent until the project made its own. The first convoy to a place called Duwald had been dispatched from Ras Tanura in September 1947, and consisted of three Diamond-T tractor-trailer combinations with loads of gasoline, oil, water, and food. The round trip took eleven days and the trucks had twenty-two flat tires. The road at that time was a winding trail, rocky most of the way and elsewhere deep in powder. The tractors were without cabs and the men learned something about driving through Arabian winds. In one section the trail wound through a dry wash and it took the convoy six hours to make 1,000 feet. Dust pockets became so deep that clouds raised by the trucks sometimes choked out the engines.

In the early stages the men generally didn't see another vehicle outside of their own convoy after the first three or four days out. The convoy system was abandoned with the arrival of super-husky Kenworth equipment, and single trucks with American drivers went through from Ras Tanura to Ras al Mish'ab in nine hours instead of days.

At the height of construction, transportation was up to 10 million ton-miles a month. Trucks were on the go twenty-four hours a day, with regular changes of crews. The trucks had radiator caps higher by inches than a tall man's head.

The mighty sand-tires, invented by Aramco's engineers to whip the desert—12-ply affairs inflated to only 6 or 12 pounds of air—plunged at the dunes like snowplows, and rode over the obstacles or through them. The vehicles hit bogs and all but sank to their beds; out from camp came the rescue hooks, and sometimes more hooks to rescue the rescue hooks, and the trucks churned on again. Often drivers saw mirages of lovely lakes and turned aside for them. One time a leader, who'd been fooled often enough, refused to turn aside, but that time it wasn't a mirage, it was honest-to-Allah water. Work for the hooks again.

While Tapline was abuilding, Bechtel used only one spread of men and machines, but it was a gang that was really spread. Portions of it were 150 miles apart.

When a man got into trouble in that world of dune and rock, he used an arm-signal code to the occasional planes that passed. He stood out in plain view with arms straight down at his sides if no help was needed; he waved down in front if he desired only mechanical help; he held arms straight out if he needed food and water; he waved both arms aloft if he wanted medical aid.

The "pleasures" of this alien desert continued to make life interesting for the men from overseas. At Ras al Mish'ab, a Yank was sitting in a tent telling of how, under similar circumstances, a fellow worker had discovered a big viper or blacksnake between his knees. At that point a tentmate remarked, "Don't look now, but there's one between yours." The narrator did look, and went out by backward somersault.

Prior to the coming of Tapline, the only water wells along the right-of-way, other than isolated wells drilled by Aramco exploration crews, were a few ancient cisterns along the caravan routes. These went dry during the summer months. Since water is a first requisite to any construction job, Aramco early in 1947 had begun drilling for Tapline's account. Ultimately twenty-five producing wells were in use—and how they were in use!—and to obtain that water it had been necessary to drill sixty holes. Some holes proved dry, and some were just bad water. The producing wells were from 200 to 1,700 feet deep. Pumps were required at all but one. Under the agreement between Tapline and the Saudi government, Tapline was obligated to furnish water free to all travelers along the pipeline route and, remembers George Colley, "it soon developed that all Bedouins were classified as travelers."

A new water hole was news of first importance to the desert tribes. As soon as the word traveled—and nobody ever did find out how it traveled so fast—large numbers of nomads moved their families, tents, and livestock over great distances to camp near the new supply. At one pump station a check was made twenty-four hours a day for two weeks and it was discovered that an average of 1,642 Arabs, 5,457 camels, and 7,195 sheep, goats, and donkeys a day used the watering trough.

By 1950 the job was going full blast with more than 1,000 Americans and 5,000 Arabs hard at it. Roy McAuliffe went in as project manager, and Roy Middleton was running pipeline construction.

Then things slowed down. A steel shortage was on at home and export permits were held up by the U. S. Government. Pipelaying was throttled down to one kilometer a day, and many of the Camel Legionnaires returned to the U.S.A. But it wasn't time wasted. During this curtailment special attention was given to on-job training of Arabs. Yank bosses were everywhere, encouraging the locals to gird up their *thaubs* and twist that wrench. Then the steel shortage ended and speed picked up again.

Throughout the crossing of Saudi Arabia the American foremen had fine practice at controlling their tongues. The Arab is a proud man, and cussing him out is the height of unwisdom. Though the hard-hat men from the New World sometimes called the headcloth-topped natives "ragheads," or "rags," it was purely for convenience and good-naturedly meant. To the Arabs, especially the Bedouin, or herdsmen Arabs, the Americans showed respect that steadily increased. The respect became honest admiration when they discovered that these untutored children of the desert were picking up ten or fifty words of English for every word of Arabic the Yanks could master.

The ways of Araby turned out to be endlessly varied, often perplexing, and always fascinating. For one thing, the Arabs themselves proved to be beyond surprising, even if the Americans were not. Lifted from a camel and placed in an airplane for his first ride through the sky, the Arab was calm as a rock. Even if, as happened, the plane hit an air pocket and dropped 1,500 feet, the passenger never batted an eye. It was all up to Allah; why worry? The dusky sons of the wind and sand also turned out to have a lively sense of humor. And though they had no national handicrafts of any kind except rough weaving and tentmaking, they took to machinery with zest.

As sections of the line neared completion, the tribesmen here and there found a new use for it. Where it swung in air across a hollow, they draped their tents over the big pipe, using it for a ridgepole, and their delight knew no bounds when the line was finished and the warmed-up oil flowed through it. For in winter the line was just a nice stove, heating the tent deliciously. When "pusher" Jim Leaver found cook fires burning under the line, which was full of several million barrels of oil, he took a dim view of these housekeeping arrangements and expelled the squatters with vigor.

West of Hafar at a spot called Hatin the problem was posed of constructing a hauling road across marine limestone beds and through clay and gypsum country beyond. This was a major undertaking. Forty Americans and several hundred Arabs went at it and continued until the Jordan border was reached. All in all, it became necessary to build a highway 930 miles long from Ras al Mish'ab to an intersection with an existing road in Jordan.

The highway across previously impassable desert is now one of the revolutionary features of the Middle East landscape. For the first time it is possible to make motor round trips between Mediterranean ports, Persia, Kuwait, and the Persian Gulf shore of Saudi Arabia. Over this road trucks now speed fruits and vegetables and other goods from the Mediterranean area to the Persian Gulf markets.

The two construction armies, the Williams forces working eastward from Sidon in Lebanon and the Bechtel spread pushing westward, joined hands in September of 1950. And there was the pipeline. It took 4,900,000 barrels of oil to fill it. In addition there had to be working stocks at intermediate pump stations. The total was 6 million barrels, which is more than the oil pumped daily from all the wells in the United States.

The long hose carries, every day, almost a third of a million barrels of oil across the deserts from the Persian Gulf to the Mediterranean Sea. The 450 miles of above-ground pipe is a happy experiment. It requires little maintenance. Rabbits and gazelles crouch in its shade. The nomad knows that it does his ancient range no harm. In the early months the tribesmen shot eight rifle holes through the strange-looking target, probably because they thought it was still carrying water (water had been used for testing). But the local authorities put trackers out and caught the marksmen, or a reasonable facsimile thereof; there have been no further pot shots in several years. In Syria, Jordan, and Lebanon the line is underground, for in those parts there is more cultivation. At places the line passes within 100 yards of the embattled Israeli border and inspectors can't approach it without a med escort. Still, while nations clash, the oil goes through. Down at Sidon, where the oil finally flows to the ships, 9 Americans, 12 Europeans, and 212 Lebanese operate the lively terminal, and a dozen tankers at a time cluster there for their loads. The storage tanks are on a hill just above the spot where tradition says Jonah landed from the whale.

The size of Tapline is hard to realize. As big around as a

large barrel, it would extend, if laid on a United States map, along the Pacific from the Mexican border almost to Canada, and the whole route would be pretty much like a traverse of Death Valley. The line includes 1,067 miles of 30-inch pipe or larger, and six major pump stations. The capacity is 317,-000 barrels of oil a day.

One day in 1956 the writer of these paragraphs sat with Lou Killian on the ruins of what had once been as busy a spot of its size as in all the Middle East. Ras al Mish'ab's work was done; it was a ghost town now. The tall legs of the skyhook still marched in from the sea but the cable sagged, the trams lay tumbled, the automatic welding contrivance that had triple-joined those hundreds of sticks of heavy pipe was sand-clogged and peeling with rust.

"She was a real sweet skyhook," murmured Lou. "Look at those uprights. Still straight and true. We could have brought the stuff ashore some other way but Burt Hull wanted a sky-hook, so, by thunder, we built him one. How those Arabs loved to ride the cars, and how they could mess things up." Nostalgia struck him. "When we got forty-eight hours' notice that some nurses—women—were coming, we built their quarters over there. Almost in forty-eight hours, we put the brick building up, and it was a dandy. Over yonder was our hospital and over there our recreation hall. We had lots of people here at one time."

Offshore, a couple of platforms stand up from the blue gulf waters where Aramco has been trying for below-sea oil, and has hit it: Safaniya field. The pair of wells, on first measurement, totaled 50,000 barrels a day, free flowing and no pumps needed, and though they might later settle down to half that production, here was definitely a lot of oil. For this and other purposes Aramco was getting ready to build a new gathering pipeline to Ras Tanura. That might mean new life, temporarily, for this ghost camp. "It would be nice," said Lou wistfully, like a father thinking about a son who has left home, "to see it all come back again."

The plane, which was on its triweekly "milk run" over Tapline, saw us down there and swooped for a landing. A camel rider humped himself hurriedly off the sandy hillock which served for a strip, and we left Ras al Mish'ab to its memories.

15

THE CAMEL LEGIONNAIRES
RIDE ON

BULLDOZERS had scarcely finished tidying up the scenery so rudely invaded by Tapline when another job fell to Bechtel's "Camel Legionnaires" and their sideboom tractors and coating and wrapping machines. Another long conduit for Middle East oil, from Kirkuk to the Mediterranean, was taken on by the Bechtel crews in combination with George Wimpey of London. The line was undertaken for Iraq Petroleum Company, British-owned, and was called the IPC.

As on Tapline, the nationals of the vicinity were utilized as much as possible. About 50 Americans and 200 Britons gave the leadership, and farmers of the Syrian-Lebanese coast and dwellers of the desert manipulated the tractors and poured out the perspiration. There were 2,500 Lebanese, Syrians, and Iraqi on the direct payroll before the job was done, and about as many more working for native subcontractors.

Whole valleys were depopulated as the line went by, their inhabitants hiring out the necessary muscle while the spreads were in their vicinity, and then handing over to the next band. They built a road in much the same way their forebears had once built one for the Romans; and they dug a trench 556

Not exactly dusty going on Lakehead pipeline extension.

Welding a string of pipe to go under Straits of Mackinac.

Shasta Dam's 9.6-mile conveyor belt climbs 26 "stairs," carrying 1,000 tons per hour across highway and countryside.

M-K of Boise tunneling under old Boston.

Beacons had to be built, then placed for Orinoco River's iron ore traffic.

Rolling out the "red carpet" — conveyor for Cerro Bolivar's ore, and below, ore cars, too, had to be brought in.

Ironing an apron for stratosphere-riding bombers at a New Hampshire air base.

Fighting time and snow in Cabinet Gorge, Idaho.

miles long, into which they dropped steel pipe big enough for a crouching man to creep through. The larger diameters, 30 and 32 inches, came from a mill near Los Angeles and there were 160,000 tons of them, requiring twenty-seven ships. The 30-inch joints were nested in the 32s or it would have taken fifty ships. It was a trick that had been worked out on the Tapline project. The nested joints, 31 feet long, weighed four tons each. Another 23,000 tons, in 26-inch diameters, came from Ohio. The Mesabi ore range of Minnesota was burrowing under Syria, which was something Queen Scheherazade never thought about when she dreamed up the *Arabian Nights*.

Most of the pipe was laid from the Mediterranean end, although a portion of it came up the Persian Gulf and overland. Working from the Mediterranean eastward, the gangs passed stone columns erected by the Phoenicians, and castles that had seen Richard Lion-Heart do battle with the infidel. It was a world where the shards of antiquity still lay about and where the crumbled civilization of the Medes seemed closer than the West's mid-twentieth century with its cranes, backhoes, draglines, and 250-horsepower trucks. It is entertaining to think that archaeologists of the future will dig up, along with Assyrian pitchers and Crusader armor, an occasional hard hat, a comic book, or a chunk of tractor tread that passed this way in its own historic moment.

A base camp was set up at Homs, north of Damascus, and the local Syrians were introduced to the conveniences of Swedish and British prefab huts. Here the heavy joints of pipe were welded into 98-foot sections, piled nine to a truck and sent off.

As the line pushed eastward, many of those prefabs at Homs picked up and followed. So did the refrigerators and air conditioners. But the Arabs, with their own ideas about housing, proved that they could make mud bricks and throw them together every bit as fast as a portable dwelling could be trundled and set up. At about 70-mile intervals new camps were established.

Crossing the great rivers of Iraq went to the forces working down from Kirkuk. The venerable Tigris was 500 feet wide at low water. The Euphrates was more formidable—1,400 feet. To cross the rivers the line was split into four parts, of 16-inch diameters, and these were snaked over by cable, while sideboom tractors waddled along and supported the steel serpents.

Rain, snow, and mud hit the pipelines, that winter of 1950–51, in a most uncommon manner, but Bechtel veterans Van Rosendahl, John Rogers, Clark Rankin, Jim Leaver, Al Berlander, Harry Waste, Roland Ross, Roy Middleton, and Joe James couldn't remember a job that hadn't hit unusual weather somewhere along the line, so they went on as scheduled.

And before long, the nationals who had dug and filled the ditch returned to their flocks or gardens. A good many of the Americans went to Canada, where oil was spurting out of Alberta wheatfields in black showers, and Interprovincial and Trans Mountain pipelines were about to be laid. But many stayed. For Steve Bechtel had much yet to do in the Middle East. By 1955 over a third of the several hundred Bechtel people in that part of the world were on their third tour of duty—a year and a half being the minimum tour according to contract. Kuwait, Basrah, Qatar, Aden—pipelines and refineries and sweat. And because of the oil that had now reached the Mediterranean shore, Mount Vesuvius looked down through its smoke to something new—a thermofor catalytic cracking unit and a catalytic polymerization unit for Socony-Vacuum Italiana near Naples. Four hundred Italians were erecting the grotesque objects, with Bechtel engineers doing the co-ordinating.

And then, in the troublous months of 1956–57 that raged about the Suez Canal after Israel, France, and Britain lunged for Egypt, with blood pressure mounting in the Arab states, three pump stations went up in shards and shreds and the flow of oil ceased abruptly in the IPC.

Europe and the rest of the world suddenly discovered what it meant when this and other pipelines, and the long lines of tankers that used to bear oil through Suez, suddenly knocked off business.

But under white tubular lights in the Bechtel drafting rooms at San Francisco and elsewhere, designers once more went to their boards. Oil would flow again. Pump stations would pump again. Bechtel men would be out stringing, wrapping, and lowering pipe again. The Camel Legionnaires would ride again, over well-known routes and over several new ones.

Oil never stops for long and the American international constructor, it would seem, never stops at all. Just shifts camp a bit.

Among the less enjoyable places of the earth is Aden, a port flanking the southern entrance to the Red Sea. British military folk shudder when they're assigned there. All is glaring sea and hot sand, and the only thing produced locally, except stringy mutton, is salt.

But it's the halfway point for steamships refueling as they ply between the extremes of the British Commonwealth, and it was the "coal hole of the East" before it became the sea-farers' gas pump. Anglo-Iranian Oil Co., Ltd., has been bunk-ering petroleum for the ships since 1919 and some 4,500 vessels call there every year. It's also a British naval anchor-age and air base.

Anglo-Iranian, since renamed British Petroleum Company, decided to build a new refining plant at Aden in 1950. A loca-tion was selected on a rocky peninsula on the other side of the bay from the existing town. When a drilling party found fresh water at 90 feet, the project was on. Speed was the order of the day, for Anglo-Iranian had just been forced out of its Abadan refinery by Premier Mossedegh.

At San Francisco, Bechtel offices worked at forced draft getting up a many-paged "scope book" of drawings and de-tail. Steve himself took this book to London. For building the big new refinery, a British firm wanted four years, and an-other American firm which was in the running wanted three. Steve offered to do it in two, with a penalty of $10,000 a day for tardiness and a bonus for finishing ahead of time. That did it. In San Francisco, New York, and London the offices of Bechtel and George Wimpey & Co., Ltd., co-venturers on this and many other enterprises, began turning out the 15,000 engineering drawings which spawned 10,000 blueprints a month, and soon they were developing such a din in the southwest tip of Arabia as hasn't been heard in the Middle East since Babel.

The result is one of the very large oil refineries of the world, with electronically controlled distillation and other fine touches; built in the teeth of sandstorms and monsoons and heat that stayed above the range of most thermometers for months at a time. A refinery and appurtenances built, port and all, by such an array of British, Dutch, Levantine, Scotch, and American bosses and subcontractors that an imposing word had to be found for them—a consortium.

For the job of putting up the giant refinery, a 120,000-barreler per stream day, Bechtel sent V. G. (Heinie) Hindmarsh as sponsoring director; J. F. Brady as project general manager; and three other Bechtel vice-presidents.

One of the first tasks was building a construction camp. The initial crew of 150 lived on a passenger liner, and put up barracks, stores, and workshops. Soon there were three small cities in full operation, housing 11,000 men. British-American-European workers had one, Levantines and Indians another, and Arabs and Somali a third, all neatly segregated to meet racial, religious, and dietary problems. A fourth encampment housed the subcontractors' people, some 3,000 of them.

Nobody in the construction business can recall another general construction camp as large and self-sufficient. Or one in which the national appetites and scruples of the workers were catered to more carefully. In consequence, the workers did an amazing amount of eating, and they all put on weight. Levantines, Indians, Arabs, and Somali never had it so good. In six months they put away 3,500,000 eggs, 1,250,000 pounds of potatoes, and 100,000 pounds of tea. They tucked away 10,000 rolls and a thousand loaves of bread a day. The various-hued boys in the hard hats and rag *gutras* and *agals* did away with a million cups of ice cream, 23,000,000 cigarettes, and 25,000 cigars. The commissary goods came in from distant countries at the rate of 500 tons a month.

All of which may have been of passing interest to bearded Qadi Bahr, a typical shepherd, seated on a knob called Wedge Hill and tending his gaunt sheep the way his ancestors had done since the Queen of Sheba ruled this land from Saba, close by, and King Solomon sent his caravans this way. Or it may all have been a plain bore to old Qadi, who perhaps preferred speculating on the slow changes of the constellations—a shepherd's specialty in the East since Abraham's day. Until the odors from construction camp cookhouses stole up the slopes of the hill, together with the fragrance of those cigarettes and ravishing cigars.

One of the situations that had to be met quite early by the contractors was what to do with Wedge Hill, the rocky peak between the refinery site and the port. A blast was indicated. And a blast it was. Thirty-four tons of explosives were planted under that dead volcano and it was at about this point that Qadi Bahr, our watching Arab shepherd, got his flock down in a hurry, and went over to the neighbor hill of Jebel Muzalkan and sold his mutton on the hoof to Yadiah Ghaylan, a fellow herdsman. Qadi explained that he'd decided to throw in with the ten thousand other Arabs he'd seen down below, lining up at the messhalls and later coming out with extremely satisfied looks.

A hundred thousand tons of the hill went up in the shot and came down in a rain of solids. This was one of the larger earth-lifting bangs put on anywhere, short of the atomic variety. A couple million yards of earth were also excavated for the refinery and many times that amount of material was shoved about by Wimpey for the breakwater, approach channel, and turning circle.

The main towers of the two crude-oil distillation units, prefabricated in France and shipped to Aden in three sections each, were designed and erected by E. B. Badger & Sons, Ltd., division of Stone & Webster, and they too were something to see as they rose into place. A hundred and forty feet high, 16 feet in diameter, and weighing 130 tons each, they were lifted one section at a time by two powerful cranes. The heaviest column was designed by Universal Oil Products Company and engineered by Bechtel. The cranes that snorted around this ungainly load probably could have lifted the Sphinx well toward the top of one of Egypt's pyramids. It was a very pretty job of skyline-changing, but once the lifting started, it was handled inside of minutes.

As if the dehydrating climate of Aden were not trying enough, making men feel as if they had been pulled through catalytic upgraders and fed into solutizer copper chloride treaters, nature tossed in a few oversized gales. A southeast monsoon hit the job with a whoosh in midsummer, 1954.

From then until September the sands of the desert broiled and eddied, ripped at human eyelids, stung hands and faces, and clotted tongues. Monsoons were followed by cloudburst. Out in one grand slap went 27 miles of road around the bay, while construction materials did a dervish whirl, and some of them are out in the Yemen desert yet. But the stuff that hadn't rolled away like hoops was collected and dusted off and 50 per cent of the refinery went on stream four months ahead of schedule, about twenty months from the day when the first of the construction forces arrived at the jobsite. Before long the whole thing was going, and the builders earned a bonus, substantial by anybody's standard, for beating their promised time. There the plant is today, one of the mightier oil refineries of the planet and a mecca in its own way that rivals, in proper times, the one at Abadan. The raw material is Kuwait or Qatar crude from the Persian Gulf. It comes by tanker and it departs by tanker or in the bellies of consuming ships.

The lights of Aden refinery at night are a beacon visible from sea for miles, and of absorbing interest to the Imam, saucer-eyed head of the state of Yemen just north of the Aden protectorate on the Red Sea. Yemen principality is rich, by

Arab standards, in green-growing things—grain, figs, quinces, pomegranates, lilacs, roses—and it is one of the few citadels of absolute personal power left on earth. The elderly, bewhiskered Imam long had hoped that it is also rich in oil, for then he could hope to rival, in some degree, his oil-rich contemporary of Saudi Arabia. But especially, he feels, he could be a man of proper importance if he could annex Aden. So there are raids, there are reprisals, there is name-calling, and there are ugly looks. So far the British lion has managed to keep this tip of his tail from being too badly chewed. More important to the immediate status of Aden was the long 1956–57 blocking of the Suez Canal. But just as pipelines are hard to extinguish permanently, so are tankers hard to discourage.

And those refinery lights are something for Yadiah Ghaylan, who bought Qadi Bahr's sheep, to ponder as he sits atop Jebel Muzalkan across the sands. When he gets tired of that, maybe he'll come down off the mountain himself and take a job with the 1,500 other Arabs and 250 Britons who permanently run the plant. After all, his fellow tribesman Qadi Bahr is doing it, and Qadi assures him that watching dials at one of the electronic control desks is twice the fun of waiting for the constellations to alter. Goes faster. Besides, there's air conditioning.

Yadiah Ghaylan will be at the personnel office tomorrow at 8 A.M.

16

THE BIG IRON-CANDY MOUNTAIN

ON JANUARY 9, 1954, a train of sixty maroon-colored ore cars clacketed down a South American mountain and rumbled to some docks. The president of Venezuela pressed a button. A stream of iron ore, rich beyond imagining, tumbled from conveyors into the hold of a ship. Far away, the new Fairless Works of U. S. Steel at Morrisville, Pennsylvania, awaited the ore ship. For the fleet of which it would be the first arrival, 100 square miles of rural Bucks County, U.S.A., had been altered with new roads, utilities, and 25,000 housing units; and big works on the Delaware River and elsewhere had been erected to produce 1,800,000 new tons of steel a year for American industry.

The button-pushing by *el presidente* fortunately did not have the catastrophic result of an earlier run, with cargo—a run not made for ceremonial purposes. That train of sixty-four cars, two engines, and a caboose "lost its brakes" and took off down the grade, skipped past all its derailing switches, and smashed into the base of the ore mountain with a thud that telescoped a half-mile string of cars into one-seventh of its original length and totally wrecked a million dollars' worth of equipment. Miraculously the only damage to human flesh was one broken leg. Bill O'Neill of M-K, who was there and who later recalled all this while sitting on a mountainside in Iran overlooking the site of Karadj Dam, recollected with pride that the Venezuela wreckage was cleared and the track open in ninety-eight hours.

Behind President Jimenez's subsequent button-pressing was a story of jungle-busting, earth moving, and plant erection which is one of the important chapters of American enterprise. Two members of the old Six Companies confederation—Bechtel and Morrison—were in it up to the tops of their seven-league boots.

For decades the industrial progress of the United States had been based upon seemingly inexhaustible deposits of iron ore. A formation known as taconite, one-third iron and two-thirds waste, stretches across northern Minnesota and on into Ontario, Quebec, and Labrador. The sheet is enriched with exceptionally high-grade pockets of fabulous names— the Cuyuna, Mesabi, and Vermillion ranges of the Lake Superior district. America's bridges, skyscrapers, hairpins, typewriters, railroads, automobiles, and telephone wires have been made from the produce of those pits; two world wars have been fought from them; steel-hulled merchant fleets and navies were lifted out of those open holes. Since the early 1900s, 80 per cent of the nation's iron ore has come from there. Men thought it could never end.

Or could it? Steel-makers began to wonder. When World War II sent us to digging and shooting away iron as never before, the steel men knew. We took 340 million tons of the highest quality reserves out of those pits to blast at Hitler and Tojo. There are still a bit over a billion tons left.

But that's getting too close to the bottom of the ore bucket.

We could easily shoot away a half-billion tons in a couple of years of another war and what would be left would be hard to reach. For all practical purposes the bucket would be bare.

Big Steel and Bethlehem and some others sent their field forces to Central America, the Caribbean, South America, and across the Atlantic in a hunt for new bonanzas of rich red earth. They roamed Newfoundland, Alaska, British Columbia, Sweden, and Africa.

The globe is not niggardly with iron, but it hides some of the largest stores in tough places. One big cache is lodged far behind a steaming Brazilian jungle in the Rio Doce region—the Valley of the Sugar River—of the state of Minas Gerais. Geologists suspect that more than one-fifth of the world's iron ore is deposited in that sweetly named area. Forty-five years ago the British undertook to bring the region into production and drove a meter-gauge railroad for 375 miles from Vitoria on the ocean to Minas on Mt. Caue. But floods washed out the roadbed, the enthusiasm of the British weakened, and the beasts and bugs of the jungle took back what they had almost let slip.

Later an organization was set up by the Brazilian government to develop the Rio Doce mines. In 1944 a joint venture of Morrison-Knudsen and Raymond Concrete Pile, calling itself Cia. Raymond-Morrison-Knudsen do Brasil, S.A., took up the first of several contracts and tackled the green hell separating the sea from Caue Mountain. They made a fair dent while funds lasted. Aid from the Export-Import Bank set up a second start in 1948 and within the following two years the earth-moving, pile-driving *senhores* from the North had rehabilitated some 280 miles of the line.

The new installment of the job got away to a watery start. It was one of the wetter rainy seasons in that section of Brazil's wet history. The sixty-five R-M-K supervisors and engineers personally manned the big tractors, shovels, and draglines and were at it eighteen hours a day. When the sun finally came out, the jungles turned into a steaming cloud. The Americans and 2,000 Brazilians tore out millions of yards of earth and rock, rammed a hundred miles of new grade through tangle and swamp, drilled tunnels, built bridges, installed switchyards and shops, and carried the railroad far up the Sugar River Valley. But until more work is authorized, Rio Doce will hold its hoard.

Geologists had also turned to Venezuela. Four hundred years ago these swamps, savannas, and forests on the northern edge of the southern continent had been searched by swashbuckling conquistadors and raffish buccaneers for gold. They came sword in hand. The modern jungle-treaders were after iron. They arrived with cameras and magnetometers. Ruins of an old Spanish furnace were found by Oliver engineers at Mundo Nuevo, not far from Ciudad Bolívar. There was no record of this furnace in the files of the Venezuelan government, but it was believed constructed 150 years before.

During the 1920s a Venezuelan, while hunting in the hills near what is now the El Pao mine owned by Bethlehem Steel Co., picked up a piece of brilliant ore and submitted it to a friend, who took it to Boecardo's hardware store in Ciudad Bolívar. Out of that incident had come a real iron "excitement" in Venezuela, with Bethlehem and other companies moving in. But the real Kimberley or Comstock Lode of the iron hunt was yet to be hit. Then, in 1945, Big Steel sent its engineers and geologists into Venezuela in earnest. An office was established at Ciudad Bolívar on the Orinoco River, and, with a nod from the Venezuelan government, survey began of a region 80 by 200 miles south of the river. This area is about the size of New Hampshire and New Jersey. Off to the northwest, coastal plains gushed with petroleum, and engineers of North American oil companies had been there some time. Along the almost unknown Guiana border to the southeast was a vague world containing, among other travelers' wonders, Angel Falls that outleaped and outboomed Yosemite and Niagara. Between the two frontiers lay low-lying grasslands with occasional high hills.

Miles of traverses were made back into the region which lies between the Caroni River, an Orinoco feeder, and the Atlantic. East of the Caroni, jungle is dense, with underbrush and vines which must be cut by machete. It was difficult to see more than a few feet. Snakes abounded. Water had to be carried in cans on burros' backs.

The men followed every known showing of ore and traced down every rumor. Hundreds of men were involved, scores of ore bodies were drilled. But nothing important was turned up. The U. S. Steel Corp. became discouraged and the whole exploration began to sag.

At this point Mack C. Lake, an M. A. Hanna Company geologist, was borrowed by Big Steel to take hold of the expedition. He was borrowed in the name of the Oliver Iron Mining Co., a Steel subsidiary.

Lake and two young field geologists, K. Burrell and Folke Kihlstedt, conceived the idea of having the area aerially photographed that lay south of the Orinoco and *west* of the Caroni, not east—an area generally considered of no promise.

Christmas Day, 1946, Messrs. Burrell and Kihlstedt were in Pittsburgh giving vice-president J. G. Munson of U. S. Steel a fight talk on spending $185,000 to take the photographs. The Big Steel executive listened, admired their steam, and took a chance. Fairchild Aerial Surveys was hired to shoot the scene.

Examination of the resulting pictures, of a scale 1 inch = 3,333 feet, showed two small mountains or hills, known locally as La Parida and Arimagua. La Parida is 50 miles south of Ciudad Bolívar, rises 1,500 feet above the plain, and is about 4½ miles long and one mile wide. Arimagua is 30 miles east of La Parida. The two hills looked interesting. On April 3, 1947, Kihlstedt and a companion named Paulik started for La Parida in a jeep. Next day they climbed the hill.

They came upon outcrops of iron ore all over La Parida and sighted long slides of ore on Arimagua. What they had stumbled upon was akin, in its rust-red way, to the valley of diamonds discovered by Sinbad the Sailor or the treasure of the Incas by Pizarro. They had walked into a mountain of sedimentary, easy-to-dig iron ore—by sober estimate the rich, great iron deposit of all history. When an expert went over it with a magnetometer, he recorded readings that he couldn't believe. Here was something for Mack Lake to write home about to vice-president Munson, and he doubtless did so with pleasure.

Diamond drills were sent for. And it was deep. By late 1947 iron-ore outcrops had been found on La Parida every few hundred feet for a distance of at least 3 miles. It was exposed in great slides for a height of 200 feet. This was 63.5 per cent pure iron.

La Parida changed its name to Cerro Bolívar, in honor of the Spanish-American liberator. The properties and other assets in Venezuela of the Oliver Iron Mining Co. were transferred to a new subsidiary of the United States Steel Corp., the Orinoco Mining Co. It was time to do things.

That brought in old friends we have been meeting wherever there is earth to be moved and concrete to be poured. It brought in Bechtel and Morrison-Knudsen, together with others who had roughed it in many an outlandish spot. The Bechtel organization was the general contractor and over-all manager. The corporate structure to handle this development work was called Constructora Bechtel, S.A. It was proposed by the steel interests to put from a quarter- to a half-billion Yankee dollars into railroads, harbors, highways, and mining and ship-loading equipment. Preparations were to be made for moving up to 10 million tons of ore a year down from the mountain for transshipment to mills in the United States.

Bechtel men toured the jobsite, returned to New York, and laid plans. They were back in Venezuela with a staff of engineers before the year was out. Temporary headquarters were in a warehouse on the ore-candy mountain.

The task ahead was to construct mining and loading facilities at the source; 91 miles of standard-gauge railroad and a highway between mine and port; a 1,131-foot steel dock, ore-crushing, stock-piling, and ship-loading facilities at Puerto Ordaz; and two towns complete—Puerto Ordaz the one, and Ciudad Piar, up on the mountain of iron, the other. A further and independent task was to dredge the rivers 178 miles for ocean ships.

Constructora Bechtel forces immediately commenced engineering work on the railroad right-of-way, improving campsites, and dozing access roads. Houseboats were made ready on the river as a floating camp.

George Colley was Bechtel headman for the work in both the U.S. and Venezuela. Roy McAuliffe was made project manager for the Venezuelan end of things, succeeded by Earl Nichols in 1952 when Roy was needed elsewhere. Ultimately Will Gerhardt, Earl's assistant, became project manager. Walt Hillman was general superintendent.

The first cargo ship from the United States arrived in March '52, with heavy equipment, and was off-loaded onto barges. It brought prefabricated barracks. By summer the camp at Puerto Ordaz was real homelike. Bechtel was responsible for planning, field engineering, administration, and supervision of all prime contractors and subcontractors other than the river dredgers. The assignment called for a lot of field engineers and there were probably more of them on the Cerro Bolívar job than on any previous Bechtel job, domestic or foreign. Administered during the life of the project were 233 contracts. The railroad and highway job, let to C. A. Morrison-Knudsen de Venezuela on January 15, 1952, was the bull-contract of the bunch, involving $23 million.

Other specialists on the project made quite a roll call: Gibbs & Hill, power plant consultants; Raymond Concrete Pile and DeLong Engineering & Construction on the docks; Gahagan Overseas Construction and McWilliams Dredging Overseas on the river-gouging; Link-Belt on the ore-handling system.

Clearing out the right-of-way for the railroad started in February. The men fought heat, rock, and mud. With May the rainy season arrived. Rain, in that region, means rain; between the dry and wet seasons the river rises 40 feet. By one sudden flood ten men were marooned for seven days and food had to be dropped to them from the air. Another time a crew sent out to rescue a truck driver found him perched on top of his water-covered truck with alligators snapping their greetings down below. Alligators or crocodiles—the 'gator is the American version and he has a shorter, broader snout. But both have a most forbidding smile and lots of teeth, as

George Colley could have told those men in Venezuela and probably did.

By midsummer everything was moving with a businesslike rumble. Hundreds of pieces of big equipment were at work all along the line—$6 million worth.

Heavy-boomed power shovels followed close behind the drilling and blasting crews, and Terra Cobra and Tournapull self-propelled scrapers and massive tractor-scraper combinations roared across the landscape. More than 2,700 Venezuelan *obreros* were working, directed by 200 supervisors. They labored around the clock to move an average of 400,000 cubic yards of earth and rock a month. They moved seven million yards, installed 13 multiple-span bridges, crushed and placed a half-million tons of rock ballast, and laid rails.

Toughest going was encountered between Miles 24 and 69 from Puerto Ordaz where excavation was entirely in rock. No ordinary rock, either; a piece of that granite tested a crushing strength of 60,000 pounds to the square inch. Ordinary drill bits had little effect. Finally bits were brought in that could do the work, and the first blast was set off. It hardly budged the hill. More blasts. Numerous pieces were too big to go into the crusher and had to be broken with dynamite placed on top. The ultimate cost of that concrete rock was $7.65 a yard. Cost in language and tempers wasn't recorded. But the rock was not yet through bedeviling the contractors and their native helpers. It wore holes through truck bodies; dipper teeth on the shovel had to be replaced twice each week. "That shovel," said one supervisor, "sure has sore gums."

The jungle also threw grass-roots trouble at the invaders. Those roots had been delving and spreading since time began. They showed up in the broken rock that was intended for concrete. At first the contractor set his men to plucking them out by hand. That kind of human toil had gone out of fashion with the Pharaohs. So the idea was hit upon of sending each load of rock down a steep chute, letting the unwanted stuff waft itself away. The ancients who invented flailing and tossing grain to separate chaff from wheat could have told H. W. Morrison's men to do that. The grass roots blew away, the rock roared down, and all was peace—almost —along the Orinoco.

Spectacular was the building of the railroad and highway grades up the long southern slope of Cerro Bolívar itself. Scores of sidehill cuts were made through hard layers of solid iron ore, almost pure metal. Nearly 200,000 cubic yards of this luscious ore were used to fill an area for a railroad marshaling yard at the top of the mountain.

The ore mountain itself found a way to club the intruders. With all that iron around, magnetic and electrical conditions were extraordinary. The permanent town that was built for mining and ore handling became a pole that attracted every stray electric ampere and static volt that happened to be roaming about. A hand could hardly touch metal without bouncing back and a tent flap couldn't be lifted without blue flashes playing. Nerves grew jumpy and so did the bodies of men. "The whole damn hill crackles and pops," gasped an often-buzzed engineer. "I bet I light up in the dark."

Norteamericanos were at work all over the scenery. One installation was the novel dock produced by the DeLong Engineering & Construction Co. under subcontract with Raymond. This dock was prefabricated in Texas in the form of three giant plate-steel barges, each 376 feet long, 82 wide, and 15 deep, equipped with jacks for self-lifting and leveling into place. They were towed across the hurricane-breeding Gulf of Mexico and Caribbean Sea to Venezuela, each barge laden with job cargo and the dock's own six-foot-diameter steel caissons. Arriving at Puerto Ordaz, the caissons were driven to bedrock to support the dock sections placed end to end, the jacks went to work, and there was the dock. It had been invented and designed by Colonel L. B. (Slim) De-Long, a former M-K construction executive.

The ore-handling system at Puerto Ordaz became a maze of steel towers, bridges, and conveyor systems. Below ground was a labyrinth of conveyor channels, reclaiming tunnels, and deep pits with ore-crushing equipment ready to grapple with 6,000 tons of ore an hour. All pushed to a whirlwind finish in four bonus months less than the 365-day time limit.

Out on the many-mouthed Orinoco, selecting one of its outlets called the Cano Macareo for "the treatment," dredge-men of Gahagan Overseas Construction and McWilliams Dredging Overseas companies dug a trough 178 miles long, with a channel 250 to 400 feet wide and 26 feet deep, for the ore fleet to the Macareo—"gooey as a macaroon," grumped one of the dredge captains—had never before been invaded by ships of depth. Many a subcontracting dredge company brought its outfits to this remaking of the South American scene.

In October 1953, the No. 1 boiler in the Puerto Ordaz powerhouse was fired. In early January 1954, the motor vessel *Tosca* received its crashing load of ore on impulse from Venezuela's button-pushing president and went chugging down to the sea. Folke Kihlstedt's lovely iron-candy mountain was in production. And the furnaces at Morrisville, Pennsylvania, 2,100 miles away, were ready and more than happy to receive.

Constructora Bechtel terminated its work something less than three years after signing the management papers. The constructors pulled out some of their equipment for jobs else-where. But much of the stuff is still there, for governmental red tape, as well as jungle vines, loves to grip what it touches.

The American engineers and supervisors went home for a few hours, to rinse out a few things and kiss the wife and meet the newest baby and be on their way again.

17

LET THERE BE LIGHT METAL

THE YEAR was 1928. In a government building in Victoria, British Columbia, a man in alpaca coat and eyeshade pored over a topographical map. He had made a discovery. His stubby finger traced contour lines slowly—and stopped. The lines were narrow loops following around and around a chain of mountain lakes. The outlet to those lakes was a river that rushed off through a steep gorge. The river lost itself in a larger stream 300 miles eastward. To the left of the map-student's halted finger the contour lines were much more crowded. They represented the steep slope of a mountain range. After reaching a summit, the lines bunched abruptly. They showed as much drop in 5 miles to westward as in that whole 300 miles to eastward. Alexander Mackenzie himself could not have been more excited, when he broke out upon Pacific tidewater after completing the first white man's journey across North America, than this poring office man with the eyeshade. He had encountered something that perhaps would remake the industrial future of western Canada. He bent to the map again. Yes, those lakes were less than 10 horizontal miles from the sea, yet were half a mile vertically above it; were held back from it only by a thin fin of rock.

The lakes could become a reservoir. A tunnel would send their overflow westward instead of east. The thunderous drop from the western mouth of such a tunnel would spin turbines. Power illimitable; power from a head of more than 2,500 feet.

Frederick William Knewstubb removed his office coat, put on a more formal garment, and went in to talk to the Minister of Lands and Forests. What he wanted was permission to lead a little field expedition. Although he was nearly sixty years old and somewhat deaf, the out-of-doors was part of his Canadian heritage.

His deductions did not stir up the minister. The lakes were 400 miles from centers of population. Transmission lines couldn't carry the tremendous surge down to Vancouver and Victoria without losing most of it. The site might as well be at the North Pole. However, if Knewstubb wanted to go and take a look, he could do so. He was granted some time off, a few men, light surveying instruments, and a small allowance. And he was off.

The maps were right. There they were, Tahtsa and four other good-sized lakes and seven smaller ones, all in a long, wide rock basin that could be made into one large reservoir; there was the Nechako River, charging eastward through its gorge on the way to economic uselessness; there were the high, slim mountains on the west, a most tempting place for a tunnel. True, it would be quite a tunnel. But against the scale of everything else around here it would merely be a hole punched through a conch shell. Knewstubb led his crew up the heights and looked over. Down there, far, far down, but not very distant horizontally, lay one of the arms of the Gardiner Canal. It was a branch of the Pacific, a fjord capable of bearing ocean ships. Up here was the stupendously high head of a lot of water, and down there was the place to spill it to. If only there was some industrial use for so much power! Well, the need would arise some day.

So the men clambered about, took readings, ran lines, sketched more maps, and when their holiday was over they boxed their instruments, shrugged into their back-packs, and left the land to the moose and beaver again. The one result of their trip was a report that went into the files. For the next twenty years it lay there, and the spruce and hemlock forests added a foot to their stretch.

Then, far off in Europe, a mouthy man with a little mustache set helmeted armies marching; and two years later bombs fell on Pearl Harbor. War all over the globe set up an unprecedented demand for metals. One of those metals was aluminum.

Some years ago aluminum was a curiosity. Telescopic drinking cups and novelty jewelry were its most familiar uses. Turning out the raw metal cost several dollars a pound. Yet it is probably the most abundant metal on the earth's surface, being an ingredient of clay. In 1886 an Ohio boy just out of college, working in a woodshed laboratory, had discovered that the separation of aluminum from aluminum oxide (alumina) could be done by stuffing a potful of prepared ore with carbon anodes, sending electricity surging through, and tapping the bottom of the pot for the molten metal.

The commercial method is more involved than that. But in that Ohio woodshed the era of light metals was born. Steadily uses were found for aluminum's strength and lightness. Toughened with alloys of copper, manganese, or magnesium, it became serviceable for engine pistons, steamship superstructure, furniture, window frames, long-distance power transmission. Being nonmagnetic, it proved valuable

for radio shielding. Nontarnishing, it makes fine protective
paint. As a powder mixed with oxide of iron, chromium, or
manganese, it is violently combustible and will melt the
toughest steel. Its powder tossed in with ammonium nitrate
makes an awesome explosive. As a metal for air frames it is
the answer to the plane builder's prayer. And each use of the
metal as a tool of war suggested a new use, equally dramatic,
when war should be followed by peace. But the manufacture
of aluminum calls for enormous quantities of electric power.
Its raw material can be profitably brought to any point where
the electricity is, provided the transportation can be done at
cheap sea-carrier rates.

The Aluminum Company of Canada, Limited, known as
Alcan, was looking for just such a site when the war ended.
For by then the era of aluminum had really revealed itself.

Knewstubb's report of 1929 was lifted out of the files in
Victoria, B.C., and dusted off. And Alcan engineers headed
for the spot he had described.

Snow lay deep on the heights above Gardiner Canal, early
in 1948, when geologists and engineers dropped off the train
at the isolated towns of Burns Lake and Vanderhoof. They
weren't telling who they were. If they were hunters, they
carried, besides their rifles, curious tripods. If fishermen,
they'd picked a peculiar season, for rivers and lakes were still
frozen.

They examined a wide area. Knewstubb's recordings of
elevations and stream flow checked out. The lakes and en-
circling mountains hadn't moved since he'd filed his report.
The backstop of mountains hadn't thickened. The drop on the
other side was still just as steep. A tunnel indeed could drop
the gather of a whole river system down to sea level a half

mile below. Here were hundreds of thousands of powerful "horses" eager to be put to work, tied up in this fastness of rock and snow. McNeely DuBose, vice-president of Alcan and its expert on power site development, knew a herd of kilowatts when he saw one. Knock a tenth of a cent off the cost of a kilowatt hour and you reduce the cost of aluminum by a cent a pound. Hundreds of millions of dollars would have to be spent, but Alcan, subsidiary of Aluminium Limited which owns subsidiaries in twenty countries, was heeled for it. The bauxite ore would be reduced to aluminum oxide at Alcan's plants in Jamaica and fed into a smelter somewhere along this forested shore.

General engineering and the practical matter of dams, tunnels, powerhouse, and transmission lines were turned over to Morrison-Knudsen.

The office and field studies of most of the project were taken in hand by British Columbia International Engineering Company, Ltd., an M-K associated corporation. A. O. Strandberg was project manager. M-K was simultaneously wrestling with fourteen major dams in Afghanistan, British Columbia, California, Wyoming, Arkansas, Arizona, Oregon, Idaho, Virginia, Labrador, and Quebec, besides tunnels, highways, airfields, canals, and railroads in various places. But Morrison's outfit put together for the Alcan project a construction army, including hardhats and Tshimshean Indians, that amounted to 6,000 men at one time, with 28,000 passing through its payrolls altogether.

Through parts of 1948 and 1949, Alcan and M-K specialists poked about. They made certain that the Gardiner Canal with its various branches would accommodate ships of deep draft. In those fjords, which are drowned canyons, the sounding line simply became lost. So far so good. Harder to find was a site for a manufacturing plant and a future city.

They located one after some far ranging. A village called Kitimat. It was on one of the many branches of the Gardiner inlet, right at sea level—a gently sloping, heavily wooded region that was much too good for the fishermen and Indians who were enjoying it. It had only one defect. Kitimat was 50 transmission-line miles from where the powerhouse would stand, and there was a range of mountains with a notch 5,000 feet high that stood dead in the way. That notch, called Kildala Pass, was wind-swept and glacier-paved.

Ahead still were the tasks of determining the exact sites for river dam, powerhouse, and transmission line. As for the dam, a site at first seemed made to order for it, but when some exploring was done to find bedrock the paradise began to fade. All was gravel and sand. It was there 200 feet down, still there at 300 feet. Then a reconnaissance party, which had pushed miles downstream, uncovered a natural site in the Grand Canyon of the Nechako.

There was a 60-mile access road to be built from Vanderhoof on the Canadian National. It would have to be slashed through bush and muskeg and grooved along rocky slopes that were designed for eagles. There were diversion tunnels and cofferdams to go in. There was cleaning of the river bed to a hound's-tooth polish. There were 45 miles of roads to be built to sources of material for the earth-fill dam itself. There was a camp to be built for a thousand men. . . .

But the damsite had been located, and among the surest things in the world was the certainty now that the dam soon would be there.

When M-K's advance construction parties had gone ashore below Kemano in 1951—Kemano is a river that comes lurching

down from Kildala Pass—the February snow was deep. Camp
was hacked out of the forests and piling for docks was
punched into the tidal flats. Barges were pulled ashore during
high tide. One tug came in from Vancouver coated with a
foot of ice. Barges soon were doing the 430 sea miles to
civilization and back every six and a half days, making hundreds of trips through all weather.

Several things about the project were unique. The dam that
would create the overhead reservoir would not be directly
above the powerhouse, but 135 miles away from it. The
powerhouse would be inside a mountain—in fact, the mountain itself would be the housing, for its pleistocene granite
would be hollowed out to form an underground hall more
than an eighth of a mile long and high as a church. The
whole project, from earth-dam on the Nechako up the reversed river and through the mountain and down through
the penstocks and around the turbines, and over the sky-high
transmission lines and into Kitimat and its furnaces, would
be a private enterprise, not governmental. It would add over
40 per cent to the current annual supply of aluminum used
by Canada and its best customer, the United States.

Roads come early on every project. A 10-mile stretch, built
for weather, was constructed from tidewater up along
Kemano River to the proposed power-generating station.
Where it bumped against DuBose Mountain, which was to be
the living powerhouse, a construction camp called Camp Five
was laid out. Within 18 months Five was quite a city, if a
fleeting one, serving as a supply base for fourteen other
camps. It had prefab houses, trailers, Quonset huts, schools,
baseball, and electricity produced by five diesel plants that
had done previous service in the hulls of submarines.

On an upland in the forest another trailer and hut camp went up, and the families of working stiffs poured in. Here Erlanders and Lloyds once more found each other, and a Kanterwitz, a Quinn, and other old neighbors from clear back to Tar Town days. The wives shared mail-order catalogues and baby lore.

All over the project, which was spread over an area the size of Vermont, New Hampshire, and Massachusetts, was M-K of Canada's Ole Strandberg, a man with a ready grin; his broad shoulders shrugged into a thick mackinaw over as many woolen shirts as needed.

Up there behind Mount DuBose, in a world of cloud, rain, snow, evergreens, rock, and silence, work started on two sites: that dam below the lower end of the lake basin and that main tunnel at its head. There was urgency about it. Work had to be pressed between spring, which comes late to the northern mountains, and fall, which comes early. M-K's Bonny, Dunn, and Strandberg knew that the organization and its subcontractors had to meet schedules or be eaten alive by costs. With snow-capped mountains all around, supply lines running off over the dip of the world, and the barometer soon dropping—to an outfit with a $179 million contract to complete, this was no place for a schedule to slip. Over at Kitimat, where city and smelter were being built by a separate group of contractors organized in Vancouver, there was similar activity. All in all, Alcan was a $450 million project, which means a lot of tree-falling and dirt-disturbing.

M-K tunneling started for diverting Nechako River. The hole went through in two months, a 32-foot bore in an arc for a quarter mile. Up went cofferdams above and below the damsite. The river bed was cleaned out and in went a concrete slab 82 feet wide and 10 feet thick. While workmen kept warm pouring this thing, others threaded the woods with roads leading off to rock and clay sources. The cliffsides were sprayed with concrete, with pins of concrete 125 feet long rammed into the walls. Thirty thousand bags of cement found a permanent resting place in the wilds of British Columbia in the process.

One of Canada's louder bangs was prepared—a shot that would open up a rock quarry. This shot took five freight cars to bring the powder to the railhead, and a lengthy caravan of nervous trucks to haul it in over the muskeg. Two hundred tons of dynamite is a lot of potential h'ist and to make a place for it, "coyote holes" were drilled two and three hundred feet into the hill. When all was ready, the holes sealed, the wives and children pulled back, and everybody behind his selected tree, the shot was fired, and a confetti of rock, some of it in 20-ton chunks, soared into the air. Before the quarrying was finished, two more shots, of 150 and 175 tons, added to the echoes of the first, and the bears which before had merely climbed trees really hightailed out of there.

Building that Kenney Dam was just building a dam, although a big one. But before the main powerhouse-feeding tunnel could be driven, a base line and triangulation points had to be laid out so that the molemen, who would work around a horseshoe curve at three or four points, could be guided toward each other. For most of the drillers the geometry and trigonometry of civil engineers was mystic medicine, but they knew that they could rely on it and would some day shake hands with each other in the heart of DuBose Mountain. The engineers laid out a base line 11,000 feet long across the spring ice of Tahtsa Lake.

Tunnel driving began a year after the initial landing down

below at Kemano, and once more it was the story of men against granite, the rock unyielding but the men unstoppable, and anyway the men equipped with drills that stabbed and explosives that mauled; with shovels and trucks of power; and with R. E. (Whitey) Davis, general tunnel superintendent, stamping about and demanding to know what the hell the boys were resting for—wasn't the boss pretty easy on them, demanding only a sixty-hour week? And down in the messhall the cooks were turning out meals to the three shifts that kept ocean steamships shuttling for more grub, and yet more. Don Gaetz, whose job down below in Camp Five included keeping track of the food that was consumed on this Alcan project, and who later was business manager for M-K's many activities in Iraq and Iran, sat on a mound near ancient Babylon one day in '56 and told about it, for the memory hadn't dimmed. Fourteen million man-meals were served, recalled Don, and they were square meals with all four corners, costing $1.06 apiece. Construction stiffs are notable self-stokers and these were mountain appetites.

The work fell into a typical M-K assembly line pattern. On came a crew; drilling proceeded for about an hour and forty-five minutes; about a hundred blast holes were chewed 15 feet deep; the drillers withdrew; the powder went in; the blast went off; and in the forty-five-minute interval while smoke and dust were clearing the drillers tucked away a hot meal. Then the muckers on the shift went to work, and the next jag of drilling began. Waste stuff went out over the nearest brink.

That for the eastern or lake end. On the west or Kemano side the point of emergence of the tunnel was pinpointed on the mountainside 2,600 feet above Camp Five. To get up there and dig from that side called for a tram, and a tram was built, a mile long with a climb of 30 degrees. Its car weighed 9 tons and its loads were up to 20 tons or 60 men, and on its first trip it carried a big International TD-24 tractor. The weight went hard with the tramline, which sagged, and the car couldn't get around a rocky knob.

Couldn't? One of the passengers proceeded to drill the rock, stuff it with powder, and set 'er off. The knob "riz and departed," the tramcar lurched ahead, and the tractor was deposited where desired. Its job was to make shelf along the granite and get the west end of the tunnel started.

Two headings weren't enough. So up the mountain the engineers went, found a suitable site for an adit, laid out a 7-mile road down to Camp Five that was a record for hairpins and jump-offs, and brought up stuff and men for opening two more headings. This midway camp was on a torrent called Horetzy Creek and the creek soon came to be called "horrific" as flash floods boomed past. And the game of playing the middle against both ends was on. The tunneling progressed three shifts a day, forty-four men to a shift. The tunnelmen once more worked from Woody Williams's jumbos, three-deckers 22 feet high, using fifteen rock drills against each heading. Shots kept going like strings of firecrackers, from two to five and a half pounds of powder for each cubic yard of muck. At fifteen minutes before midnight on September 27, 1952, a swing shift rested its tools and Red Hostetter, superintendent of west portal operations, looked back on 248 lineal feet of 25-foot tunnel delivered by his galaxy of talent in six action-crammed days. His boys had topped by 7 feet the old record for a week's work which had been made on a dam tunnel in California, back in 1949.

October's end was set for the joining of hands through the tunnel. The hope became a fixed goal when all tunneling rec-

ords for comparable rock and bore again had been broken—
61 feet of diorite granite in one day, 282 in the week.

A final blast, and Ted Leonard, tunnel superintendent at
West Tahtsa, scrambled through to shake hands with Whitey
Davis. The mountain above their heads had been kept danc-
ing with never-ending shots of dynamite and the jar of jack-
hammers, and now the tunnel was through, with more than
2 miles of it braced by steel arches where it passed under a
mountain lake. The two headings were within 6 inches of
perfect alignment and 3 inches of grade. That's shooting
through miles of rock, going around curves, and hitting the
bull's-eye near enough.

Meanwhile the powerhouse. This lair was to be 710 feet
long and 81 feet wide, with an arched roof 118 feet above
the floor. The fact that it was hewed out of the living rock,
instead of erected out under the sky, was not novel. There
have been underground powerhouses since 1898, when engineers gophered one at Snoqualmie Falls, Washington, to
avoid ice and spray from the falls. Among the advantages of
such burrowlike housings are dense foundation, freedom from
structural maintenance, and, at Kemano, the fact that construction could be kept up in winter when outdoor work
suspended. In addition, there was no menace of avalanching
snows and rock on the finished structure. Finally, such powerhouse and penstocks would be pretty secure from enemy air
action.

M-K had been building scooped-out powerhouses in several places, though not on this scale. Into the mountain went
some access and tailrace tunnels. The crown of the roof or
ceiling was next excavated and concreted. Working from the
ceiling down, the men had the unremoved core to stand on.
Then the long vertical cuts for the "walls" were made. Dozers

tore and shoved; shovels raked and scooped; trucks took their loads; the din of diesels and shots kept eardrums aching; and the cathedral of the turbines took form. By the time the unwanted portion of the mountain had been hauled out, a variety of other tunnels had been driven for penstocks and connecting purposes, and the steel for lining then began coming up from Vancouver. These penstocks were 11 feet in diameter and they slanted down from the main tunnel at a 48-degree angle, carried a thousand feet downward to the 1,600-foot level, moved horizontally for another 1,100 feet, and then made the dive for the turbines, each penstock dividing into four to serve eight turbines in all.

Three of the turbines, powering three generators, went in and were ready to operate in the spring of '54. They tossed off an initial load of 420,000 horsepower. The second phase of the development called for 1,120,000 horses in the underground barn and the general plan allows for an ultimate 2,240,000, and M-K is still at work, under new contracts. The final result will be just under Grand Coulee's horsepower, which is 2,250,000. It would be enough to light and energize Vancouver, Winnipeg, Toronto, and Montreal all put together. Even the opening phase of the development produced power sufficient to turn all the wheels in Vancouver and Victoria combined.

Dam, tunnels, and powerhouse were routine compared to what was going on in the valley of Kemano River and up over Kildala Pass. The writers of this book asked Harry Morrison what he regarded as the outstanding feature of this, his construction job of jobs, and he replied instantly: "Those transmission towers." The erectors had to make mountain crags sprout towers as housetops sprout TV antennae, and they had to do it with hobnails, crampons, pitons, and all the paraphernalia of a score of Everest expeditions, hanging to cliffs and lying out on ledges in the face of blizzards and getting supplies by air drops. "Those fellows," says Morrison, who has made a specialty for half a century of hiring raw courage wholesale, "were the most courageous men I have ever known."

In that 50 miles lie two canyons, one running up to the pass and the other running down the other side. The way up was by cataract and icefall and avalanche chute and rockfall. Corrugated country. To investigate and map and compare the possible tower sites by ground travel might have been accomplished in four or five years. It was done in weeks, with helicopters. Carl Agar and his Okanagan Helicopters Limited of Vancouver had been spraying orchards and scouting pipelines when this survey job, together with the construction job that followed it, was tossed into his lap. Agar's little Bell copters climbed up there, with engineer sitting beside pilot in the plastic bubble. The ravines fell away and the peaks fell away and the avalanches went on thudding far below, and the forests looked like green lawns—and the route was mapped. But Carl Agar's eyes screwed up as he contemplated what was still ahead for him. Three hundred and six transmission towers were to be scattered along, many of them on pointed crags. He might undertake to land a copter on a stone needle; but taking off, at 5,300 feet above sea level, would be something else. His pilots would just have to learn to shove the whirlybirds over the brink, like a boy jumping off a shed roof with an umbrella. . . .

Thirty-nine towers were of aluminum—four or more tubular legs joined by a crossbar and the legs set strongly in every slanting direction that would defeat the winds. Insulators were twice the height of the men who hoisted them into place.

The line, of 2¼-inch steel-cored aluminum, was built to carry 300,000 volts. No transmission line had ever been thrown over such terrain, or one to carry such voltage. And though the installation of additional generators in the powerhouse was something for the future, the transmission line itself had to be set up for the whole ultimate load right then and there. A second line just couldn't be put through with the original line occupying the pass and carrying such current.

The towers could not be spaced with the neat evenness that appeals to men sitting at drawing boards. They had to go where there was a perch for them. This the transit men had arranged for, spying out ledges and points where the towers would be in reasonable line, with a logical chance of standing up to the gales and snow.

The tower erectors and linesmen were shown those shelves and pinnacles and invited to get up there. Some did it with fingers and toes. Others rode in by copter. Once up, the boys stayed, sometimes for weeks. To supply them, Agar's copter fleet put on one of the more spectacular shows since Kittyhawk, Burma Road, and Berlin air lift. Most of the stuff that came up was slung from ropes under the body of the aircraft and, while the flutterbug hovered, the men detached their grub and prefab houses and work gear. Unloading had to be done at top speed, and anything that was fragile came packed in sawdust. After a bit of experiment, popcorn as a shock insulation was found to be more resilient, and after that, popcorn it was. The copters grew so used to pinpointing their targets and staying over them that they took to loading on the wing as well as unloading. At the pickup area everything waited strapped to wooden pallets aboard trucks. Over came the whirlybird, its blades revolving; up went the pallet on a forklift; around it went the load rope; and away went the cop.

Between visits from the birdmen, the crews put the towers up and anchored them, strung their transmission cables, hallooed to each other across space, and with one leg hooked around a crossarm leaned out and shook hands with the angels. When not working they looked at the view. Or perhaps preferred not to.

Meanwhile a road was being pushed up the steeply angled floor of Komano Valley, to serve construction camps and supply depots for the towers that didn't have to be perched on pinnacles. One night a 75-foot stretch of construction line was knocked out by an avalanche while the men of Camp Ten were asleep. The roar was heard from top to bottom of Kemano Valley. At dawn a couple of men scurried to see what, if anything, was left of a compressor and tractor that had been at work up there the day before. The machines were still in place, but they were now on the far side of a 70-foot abyss filled with nothing but crisp mountain air. That called for alpine work. Down and across and up the chasm the men carried lines. A cableway was soon in operation, rock uncovered by the slide was blasted out of the way, and timbers were sent for. The lumberjacks who went into the woods must have carried Bunyan's saws and axes, for the girders that came out were 100 feet long and 3 feet thick. These were winched across until they straddled the gap. "Small" trees were crosslashed for planking. Bulldozers followed, laying a foot of gravel. Ten days after the snowslide, there was a catwalk for the tractors. Work on the road duly proceeded.

This on the Kemano or south side. On the north tractors hacked and bunted from the summit downward. At the bottom of Kildala River, the opposite number of Kemano River, other tractors were bucking upward. The woods and gorges rang with the clamor of deep-lunged engines and thudded with dynamite. By December of '52 all ends of the access road from Kitimat to Kemano up and over Kildala Pass had been picked up and tied together. The erection of Kitimat smelter and city was meanwhile being handled by a group of eight Canadian contractors.

By the spring of 1954 the work of three years was 90 per cent complete. Each phase of the half-billion dollar project had been a major construction task. Kenney Dam's rock-and-earth fill, 317 feet high and 1,500 feet long, held the once noisy Nechako River in firm check. At the western end of the reservoir the 10-mile tunnel stabbed through the mountain, drawing the 25-foot-thick torrent of water with it. The penstock tunnels were preparing to dump the water down to the west. The great powerhouse cavern within the rock heart of the mountain was all set. A switch was flipped. Power from the first two of many generators went surging over the line to Kitimat.

In their initial year the furnaces turned out 83,000 tons of aluminum. This was for practice. Then nature rose up and kicked two or three of those transmission towers down the gulch, bowling them out of the way with an avalanche. Painfully they were restored. And the potlines of Kitimat were cooking again.

Probably the fight with Kildala Pass never will be completely won. But when all of Kemano powerhouse's generators are humming, and all of Kitimat's pots are stewing, there will come such a flood of aluminum as the world has never seen. By that time Kitimat is expected to be the third city of British Columbia, and the beaver, ermine, and elk will be gone far away from the high hills behind Gardiner Canal.

Just about gone, too, is the memory of Frederick William Knewstubb. While dams and mountains have been receiving the names of Alcan officials, he's the forgotten man. They ought to cast him in aluminum, eyeshade and alpaca coat and all, and stand him up there on a pinnacle. His vision foresaw much of this, and he should be permitted to behold it forever with a stainless and rustproof gaze.

18

A CUP OF WATER FOR AUSTRALIA

DOWN in Australia they call a good thing "right as rain." Rainwater is of prime importance to the island continent, most of which has too little of it. The eastern edge gets 40 to 80 inches and the southeast tip intercepts the southeast trade winds and has decided use for an umbrella, but even here conservation is important, for nature has denied the land lofty mountains and big lakes to hold back the deluges for the dry months.

In past years an earth-fill dam, the Eildon, was flung across Gouldburn River 80 miles northeast of Melbourne. It created a reservoir of some 300,000 acre-feet. But in 1950 the Rivers & Water Supply Commission of the state of Victoria decided that that dam must go higher, much higher. American damsters were summoned and Lester Corey bagged the contract for his Utah Construction Company. The order was to pile a new or Big Eildon earth fill on top of the elder or Little Eildon and make the lake nine times larger. It was to be the number one dam, for size, in all the Southern Hemisphere, backing up 2,750,000 acre-feet of water, with a surface of 53 square miles; operating a powerhouse; and creating irrigation facilities for thousands of acres of thirsty land.

Here was a familiar dish for Utah Construction Company. Down from the West coast of the United States and across the Pacific hurried the diesel-powered hooks and buckets and trucks, the dozers and rippers and cranes that would lift a chunk of Australia out of a river bed and put it where it would be useful.

For four and a half years the people of Melbourne streamed out to watch the work go forward on the Gouldburn; to picnic and scramble about and inform each other that the Great Pyramid of Egypt had contained only 3,500,000 cubic yards of rock, but this structure was going to contain 14 million; that before it rose, 17,500,000 yards had to be excavated; that the Chinese, who also claimed to be builders, could now just forget their Great Wall—this wedge in the middle of a river had enough stuff in it to build a wall 30 feet high from Melbourne to Adelaide. The citizens ranged the job, viewed the trucks, regarded cranes that could bite 6 tons at a nip, heard that 2,000 tons of explosive were being used to make the skin of old earth quiver; and reminded each other that they were standing on top of the second tunnel, for length, in any land. Horse racing, a sport of sports in Australia, took a back place when the powder was tamped for the 145,000 tons of rock that were to be blown down in one blast. Off went the charge on schedule, and down came the shower of cobbles, right as rain.

These were statistics to make every citizen of the southern continent stand taller. But Utah was thinking about the terms of its contract, which said that this work was to be done in four years and thirty-six weeks. For suddenly the most important nozzle in construction, the financial one, had been given a hard right turn. Loan funds to keep the job going died down to a drip. The cranes, trucks, and shovels went idle and dynamite shots ceased echoing in the valley. The equivalent of a working year was lost. But then the financial hose spouted again, to an ultimate total of £15 million or U.S. $33,800,000. Work leaped ahead, the dam rose and was finished and polished off with grass and viewpoints and picnic tables, and Big Eildon was ready for the handing over, three months ahead of the original schedule and in spite of difficulties. The Wattis brothers and Hank Lawler, who'd built many a dam with Utah stamped upon it, had handed on their tradition to the land down under. Now the big plug stands, controlling floods, preventing drought, providing cheap power, creating farms, and establishing new livings for 100,000 people. Right as rain.

Utah has since taken on a multimillion-dollar contract for the construction of an ammunition plant for the Australian Department of Defense near Sydney, and in 1956 the old strip miner of the Utah hills hauled on his boots and tackled a huge mine and plant expansion program for Mt. Isa Mines, Limited, a copper, lead, zinc, and silver producer 1,300 miles north of Melbourne.

One hundred miles north of Melbourne, Morrison-Knudsen is also sponsoring a stretch of Australia's ambitious irrigation program. It is building forty-three bridges, siphons, and other concrete structures along a canal known as the East Gouldburn Main Channel. To handle it for M-K and McDonald Constructions Party, Limited, as M-K's local partner is oddly called, Mac T. Hardwick hopped over from Mocuzari Dam in Mexico with one of those kangaroo hops that construction men make at the rustle of a contract.

Halfway between Melbourne and Sydney, in the southeast corner of Australia, are the Snowy Mountains of the Great Dividing Range. In trade-wind season they collect water which, through time immemorial, has wasted away into the already sufficiently watery Tasman Sea. Australia had eyed those spendthrift rivers long enough. The National Development Minister got in touch with the U. S. State Department; State got U. S. Bureau of Reclamation on the phone, and the Bureau, which is not given to turning down reclamation projects, joyfully found itself drawing up plans. This was a friendly act performed by one nation for another, somewhat similar to the way Australia teaches the U.S. how to play tennis; but this project, when finished, would turn Snowy River and its main tributaries completely around and send them under the barrier range to the arid lands on the west. It would be the ace construction contract so far ever offered to private enterprise by the island continent.

When contractors of the U.S. and Europe got the word, there was a flurry of co-venturing alignments, and the job was carried off by a group led by the Kaiser Engineers division of Henry J. Kaiser Company, Kaiser's associates being Walsh of New York, Perini of Massachusetts, Raymond of New York, General of Seattle, Bates & Rogers of Chicago, and the Arthur A. Johnson Corporation of New York. The first two major contracts, for $60 million worth of dams, tunnels, and appurtenances, got started within weeks of the letting of the 1954 contract.

George Havas, vice-president and general manager of Kaiser Engineers, saw this project immediately as one of the important developments in the history of Australia and of the engineering world. He sent up to Hanford in Washington and told John Tacke, resident manager for a $110 million construction contract at the plutonium works, that John was off for the land of the wombat, the wallaby, and the bandicoot and that he could take a few hours to get ready if need be, but minutes would be better.

John Tacke is a spectacled man with receding hair and a pugnacious profile and he is used to having large orders hurled at him, and to catching them like an end going up for a forward pass. He'd been a concrete foreman at Hoover Dam, general superintendent during the construction of the wartime Kaiser Shipyards, and from that elephantine task had moved on to the mastodon job of building the ships themselves. Later he'd supervised operation of Kaiser's Willow Run auto assembly plants. He was off for the Southern Hemisphere almost before he could learn whether antipodes were heavenly bodies or a kind of fish. Arriving, he spread the blueprints out, found where the Eucumbene and Tumut rivers were, toured the ground, set up his railhead at an old coastal gold-rush town called Cooma some 250 miles south of Sydney, and looked over the crew that had begun gathering. Between April and November, besides seeing to the construction of whole towns around his living and supply areas, he handpicked as keen a body of molemen as ever reamed a mountain range. About half of them were old Aussies and the others were "New Australians," invited in, as permanent residents, from Germany, Sweden, Holland, Italy, Yugoslavia, Spain, and North America. All raring to go.

Summer comes in November down there under the Southern Cross, and winter comes in July. Tacke's gangs climbed the steel scaffolding of their rail-mounted jumbos and began making hole. The word that was passed around was a familiar one to men who had burrowed mountains. It was "Get underground before winter so you can keep working no matter how bad it gets upstairs."

Eucumbene Portal Camp, 60 miles by road from Cooma, was where the drillers bit in. By November 1954, some 250 or so were punching, shooting, mucking, and hauling at that heading and by April, when the people of the region began getting out their long john underwear, the bore was in 1,700 feet. Others were making a road that wound like a hoopsnake over the Snowy Mountains which, incidentally, soon merited their name. Ten miles from Eucumbene Portal a river was diverted and a 300-foot junction shaft was dropped to the main tunnel level. Down this shaft men and equipment were lowered, including an entire electric locomotive and the tracks to run it on. Some 450 men began pecking toward the Eucumbene crews who were gnawing at the rock many miles away. TNT whumped, rock lurched, rail cars charged in, the artery inched ahead, and tunnel technicians placed the steel supporting beams where needed, usually 4 feet apart but sometimes at 2-foot intervals. Thanks to careful planning by the paper-work people, no ventilation difficulties arose.

Australia was properly fascinated by these doings. Wrote one Sydney newspaper scribe, "Not often do engineers engineer down under, Down Under."

When winter did arrive, Snowy's tunnelers moved with the care that men learn to exercise in lightning season. Nobody wants to be tamping TNT into an 8-foot powder hole and have nature quicken it to life with a bolt of her own. At the least suggestion of an electric storm outside, the powdermen made like the great Australian kangaroo, only faster.

The winter had another muleshoe in its fist, wrapped softly in its large white glove. The worst blizzard in twenty years swung a haymaker, trapping the underground workers and smothering the surface. Six large camps were hit hard, and no new food came in for a week.

Second summer found crews at two more headings. A good day's average penetration was 30 feet. And then the Kaiser-led boys started making real hole. They heard what H. W. Morrison's men had been doing on that Alcan project in British Columbia and they began throwing records of their own around. With a combination of American, Australian, British, and Swedish equipment and an improved drilling-blasting-mucking cycle, they tore into the mountain like ter-riers after a gopher. May 1955, which just about marked the approaching rumbles of the second winter, saw a proud world's record set up of 481 feet in six days. This on a bore of 24-foot diameter through slate and quartzite resting on granite. The advance was made by 144 men working in three shifts, under C. C. Turner, general tunnel superintendent, and J. C. Hester, Eucumbene heading boss. The best one day's advance, 81 feet, was also a record. It may safely be assumed that they let Morrison-Knudsen's boys know about it, up there on British Columbia's Gardiner Inlet. When Kaiser's outfit busted out into sunlight at the end of the main underground route, they'd broken the ground for a 14-mile concrete-lined hydraulic tunnel.

During the second year a subterranean plant was built at the bottom of Junction Shaft and the coring of the big tube went foreward in two directions. Ground was also cleared outside for the 100-foot high diversion dam which would route summit waters down through the shaft and into the main tunnel. Elsewhere the workers in this isolated region were getting on with a concrete-arch main dam. The joint venturers, from their pool of manpower, were able to put men on these tasks who had built Hoover and Grand Coulee dams and powerhouses, Bonneville Dam, Detroit and Hungry Horse dams and powerhouses, the East Delaware aqueduct, and the huge Sir Adam Beck hydraulic pressure tunnels under the city of Niagara Falls, Ontario. It was first-rate skill sent overseas to augment the local hand and brain supply, and a good example of how nations, working together through private enterprise, can lever mountains aside and twist rivers around for mankind's benefit.

The work didn't end with the 14-mile tunnel. There were Eucumbene River to block and the reservoir of 3,500,000 acre-feet to be created. This called for Adaminaby Dam, half a mile thick and containing 9 million cubic yards, to store the equivalent of eight times the water in Sydney harbor. A town had to be moved. The same group of joint venturers under Kaiser Engineers sponsorship picked up the contract in June 1956, to complete this phase of Snowy Mountain project by 1960. Elsewhere on the hydroelectric development, Norwegian and French interests are also at work.

When all is completed, the Snowy Mountain project will have 85 miles of tunnels, 7 major dams, 17 major power stations, 400 miles of aqueducts, and 3 million kilowatts leaping out over the transmission lines. This exceeds the capacity of all generating stations operating in Australia prior to Snowy. The plan is one of the world's larger water development projects. It will considerably remake one section of the island which, in another section, has been hitting oil in quantity. Australia is on its way.

19

HEALTH, JEEPS, STEEL, ALUMINUM—AND HENRY

ALONG with U.S. industry in general, the Kaiser companies in the war years borrowed heartily in Washington. And in the immediate postwar period Kaiser leased and later purchased several war surplus plants. With bargains to be had for a song, his bass voice lifted like a bassoon. The net result of the general dispersal of the war plants was to keep America in production and the economic top spinning. Kaiser's government loans were almost entirely paid off, with interest, by 1950. He has borrowed since then, widely and handsomely. But it has been from commercial banks and insurance companies. Further financing has come through the plowing-back of profits and public issues of stock.

Edgar Kaiser and Clay Bedford were two of a group of young men to whom the headman tossed his plans for execution. And plans he was constantly cooking up.

Health Plans, for instance. The idea of prepaid medical care seems to have come at construction of the Los Angeles aqueduct, when the chief medical officer, Dr. Sidney Garfield, developed such care on an insurance basis. Kaiser followed with a prepaid health plan at Grand Coulee and elsewhere, costing a man 50 cents a week. From this his thoughts went winging to "Mayo Clinics for the Common Man," not necessarily tied in with the projects he was running. He foresaw doctors getting together in hospital health centers, and the public participating.

His engineers, who could estimate the 8-yard buckets of concrete in a mile-long dam, who could figure the rivets in a hull and the horsepower in a cataract, were swung around to the job of figuring the average man's insurance rate for the hour the doctor cometh. It worked out at slightly more than a dime a day. The Kaiser Foundation Health Plan, originally called the Permanente Foundation, was set up by Henry J. and the first Mrs. Kaiser as a charitable trust and, after the war, was thrown open to the public generally. The upshot has been a chain of hospitals and clinics, currently numbering fifty-one, that spread over four western states. Two million patients a year pass through the wide glass doors.

Four decades ago Henry Kaiser could keep track of his business in his head, or with a pencil on a shingle, but today it takes an electric computer to deal with the figures; a work force of about 70,000 people; a payroll of $225 million; 90 plants and facilities in seventeen states and territories and some ten foreign countries, turning out 300 products. The operations are as diverse as mining coal and spinning aluminum wire, making airframes, and giving brand-new babies their first spanking.

Kaiser industries built 5 million motor vehicles, though that phase of the Kaiser adventure has been a headache. Kaiser industries have made enough cement to pave the equator with a two-lane highway—and Henry is strong for wide highways. The industries as a group are one of the first thirty in the United States for size.

A concrete necklace for a lovely river's throat — Cabinet Gorge.

A little something in steel for Seyhan Dam, Turkey.

Box Canyon on Clark's Fork, Idaho — another fight against time.

Kajakai Dam in faraway Afghanistan; power going to waste.

Karadj Gorge in Iran, which will slake Teheran's thirst.

Making way for Iran's Karadj Dam. Beyond lies Caspian Sea.

Hungry Horse Dam rises in Montana's old Wild West country.

Hungry Horse on the Flathead, 564 feet high — the third highest.

They are a diverse family of activities knit together by the interest in each company that is held by Kaiser Industries Corporation, which now wholly owns the Henry J. Kaiser Company that Kaiser founded in 1914. To sound off the corporations partially owned by Henry J. Kaiser Company and under Kaiser management, all America with its hills, fields, mines, deserts, mountain peaks, and cities seems to roll past like a cyclorama: aluminum and chemical, steel, cement, metal products, construction, commercial vehicles.

Four of the companies—Kaiser Aluminum & Chemical Corporation, Kaiser Steel Corporation, Permanente Cement Company, and Kaiser Industries Corporation—are publicly owned companies with 70,000 stockholders. Kaiser Metal Products, Inc., is privately shared with Sears Roebuck & Company. The cement company, with its offshoots Kaiser Gypsum, Permanente Steamship, and Glacier Sand and Gravel, has among its directors the heads of firms frequent in this book— Utah's Allen Christensen, M-K's H. W. Morrison, J. F. Shea's G. J. Shea, and General Construction's D. V. McEachern.

The trunk to the Kaiser industrial tree retains as "operating divisions" the sand and gravel business which is the historic foundation of all Kaiserdom; the Kaiser Engineers, who are spectacular; and Willys Motors, Inc.

The veteran member of Kaiser's team is A. B. Ordway, who was with Henry long before the Hoover Dam days. Once Ord was driving in northern California and discovered that bids were being called on a highway job. He flashed the word to Henry J. The two caught the first train down to the jobsite between Redding and Red Bluff, but the train wouldn't stop. Kaiser said, "This must be it," and he swung off in the dark. Ordway heard Henry J. smack something solid. Could have been a tree. It was a poor place to detrain, and Ordway

had a new suit on, but he couldn't leave his associate im-
paled somewhere like a cone on a pine, so he swung off
too, hit an embankment, rolled, lost much of his new suit,
and located Henry J., who was only slightly knocked out of
breath. They inspected the jobsite, won the bidding, moved
to California permanently in 1921, and have been together
ever since.

While in Cuba on the highway job that gave him his first
big money, Kaiser made the acquaintance of George Havas,
who was engineer on a sugar plantation. Kaiser's judgment
told him to hang onto Havas, who'd picked up his engineering
degree in the technical college at Stuttgart, Germany, but
had a stock of private genius to guide him where the book
leaves off. Ordway is vice-president of Kaiser Industries and
manages Kaiser Center today, and George Havas is vice-
president, general manager, and chief engineer of Kaiser Engineers division of the Henry J. Kaiser Company. Under
Havas, all things which Henry J. alone considered possible
have a way of becoming quite thoroughly practical.

Havas is a tight-thinking man with glasses, a small mustache, and a dab of hair up top that looks like a reflection of
the ornament on his lip. His caution is the balance to Kaiser's
daring. "Those sheep have just been shorn," announced
Henry J. one day as they were train-riding through rural
country. After examining the flock from the train window,
"Yes, Mr. Kaiser," conceded George reluctantly, since he
didn't have all the facts. "It does look that way from this
side."

At the home office in Oakland, California, Havas has nearly
a thousand engineers, technical experts, and staff people, and
what they won't tackle hasn't been discovered. These are the
midnight oil boys who sail into the research, preliminary

studies, design, layout, estimating, readying of specifications, contract negotiating, procurement, and expediting. Under programs set by these heavy thinkers, construction men put up breakwaters, chemical and industrial plants, airports, and houses; dig tunnels, strew highways, fling bridges, and change the face of the land like plastic surgeons, along with wading to their necks in atomic energy projects. Besides this staff at home, George has about 5,000 more people in the field.

The main headquarters of Kaiserdom for a dozen years, soon to be replaced with splendor, is an eleven-story building on Oakland's Broadway. It is a place of plate-glass partitions so clear and apparently doorless that a visitor moves sleep-walker-fashion with his arm out; of curving reception desks and curvesome receptionists; of ankle-deep carpets and the silence of Pyramids. The important offices are padded in leather, and gents with multimillion projects on their minds rush around in shirtsleeves. Henry J.'s own office is not an overlarge room and he, unlike some of the other major figures in this book, doesn't go in for maps; he likes the view of hills, homes, and water. A chief item on his desk is a festoon of telephones, enough for a committee to hunch up to. The telephones are for use when the boss wants to hold a nationwide conference by wire, which is frequently. As a phone customer, Henry Kaiser is probably the number one user of all time.

Until he took on the automobile industry for an adversary, Kaiser was pretty well justified in feeling that he could do anything. He decided to plunge into motorcar manufacturing in 1945. Motorcars looked like a natural to a man who liked to combine engineering with assembly line production. For salesmanship and the management of production he took, as partner, Joe Frazer of Willys-Overland and Graham-Paige.

In eight months from scratch he had his auto factory in production at Willow Run and its output was no small thing.

In the junglelike ambushes of Detroit, General Motors proved to be no gorilla—it even lent a helping hand, offering the newcomer Hydromatics and needed gearboxes and good advice. But trouble aimed its blowguns at Henry and Joe from behind every tree. They had to take surplus labor with its lesser skills. Suppliers wouldn't come up with the supplies. Steel had to be swapped around for or made by Kaiser; the industry seemed to be holding out on him. Auto-making executives who knew all the answers refused to be lured out of their comfortable GM, Ford, Studebaker, and Packard caves. And good well-heeled dealers were as hard to find as willing stockholders had been easy. In its first five years K-F lost $34 million. Joe Frazer went out. The West Coast Kaiser management men, who'd come East to make Willow Run run, struggled manfully.

"This is the roughest thing we ever tackled," said Edgar Kaiser in '51, even though he'd sold 151,000 cars in the previous year and grossed $238 million.

But the Kaisers were determined to make another success. They put up $72 million and acquired the business and plants of 50-year-old Willys-Overland Motors, Inc. They changed over to production of the famous jeep and commercial vehicles, became the number three exporter of commercial vehicles, and branched out with Kaiser Aircraft and Electronics into precision-machined parts for jet aircraft and development of new cathode-ray tubes. The effect of the last-named may be that your future TV set will have flat tubes and hang like a framed picture from your wall. They established, in Argentina, the first automotive manufacturing industry in South America, as distinct from just an assembly plant. Within a twelvemonth Kaiser Engineers spearheaded the completion of a factory to turn out annually on one shift 40,000 jeeps, passenger cars, trucks, and station wagons. Despite tumbling dictatorships and revolutions, the riders of the pampas in 1956 began throwing their loops from Kaiser-made jeeps in quantity. The outfit arranged similar projects in other Latin-American countries, in addition to Willys assembly plants in the Netherlands, Israel, Turkey, Australia, India, Japan, Mexico, France, and South Africa. Their automotive business turned in a profit in 1955–56. There was, to use a metaphor, some dancing in the streets over that one.

A major step in turning the automotive walloping into a happy recovery was the formation of Kaiser Industries Corporation, new name of Kaiser Motors. The Kaiser family and key men put all their holdings of the Henry J. Kaiser Company, including Kaiser Aluminum, Kaiser Steel, and Permanente Cement stocks, with a market value of $332,500,000, into the new corporation. In that way, stockholders of the old Kaiser Motors received a share of ownership in other Kaiser-affiliated companies. Besides turning the automobile adventure into black ink, the Kaisers thus could claim to have rebuilt the corporate base for future expansion in a score of industries and heavy construction. Masterminding this arrangement was the E. E. (Gene) Trefethen, Jr., who, fresh from University of California and Harvard Business School, had started out with Edgar as a laborer in the sand and gravel plant, traveled with Henry J. as his executive assistant, and become the executive vice-president and management-financial brain in virtually all the boss's companies.

Kaiser's proud war baby, Fontana steel plant, had brought fully integrated steelmaking to the West Coast, and the many-chimneyed plant that stands in the orange groves today is like nothing else anywhere. It occupies a 1,800-acre site 45 miles from Los Angeles. Current expansion will double its capacity to three million tons annually, giving it predominance west of the Mississippi. Its nine rolling mills lead for diversification. Everything is western, from the coking coal mines in Utah and New Mexico to the iron ore over near California's Palm Springs; from the cowboy hats on some of the mill hands to the view of the San Bernardino Mountains from the front door. The hot Mojave Desert is up behind the mountains, and the cool Pacific Ocean an hour and a half away, with Hollywood midway. Kaiser Steel Corporation, managed by Jack Ashby, is a privately financed company with 21,000 stockholders, an investment approaching $400 million, and a program for expansion by 40 per cent. Its 11,000 workers enjoy living in the San Bernardino Valley, a lovely spot which they stain and smog up as little as possible, thanks to smog-control equipment.

"Wait until he runs out of ore," chanted the skeptics. But Henry didn't run out of ore. His scouts did some scouting and turned up Eagle Mountain, practically in Fontana's back yard as ore hauls are measured.

Eagle Mountain was first discovered back in the 1890s by a pair of gold seekers. Their picks didn't uncover much gold, but every ton of rock they sifted, to get half an ounce of yellow metal, consisted of 54 per cent raw iron. The heap lay out in the simmer and blister of the Salton Sea area and it was there, rich but unmined, when Fontana steel mill rose 164 miles away. To cross 50 of those miles and tie in with the Southern Pacific's rails called for a private railroad, so one was built, the Kaiser construction forces taking it from 1,658 feet above sea level to 190 feet below, battling with the desert of the Colorado until, 9,500 tons of rails and eighteen bridges later, the cars were at the main line en route to the mill.

Relieved of worries about supply, Fontana belches forth pig iron from three blast furnaces, and plates, pipe, tin plate, strip, shapes, bars, and everything else that Vulcan did or didn't think of.

The latest novelty Fontana has unveiled is an oxygen converter, licensed in the U.S. to Kaiser Engineers by its Swiss patentees, which refines molten pig iron into steel. A jet of oxygen generates dust-laden gases at a temperature of 3,000 degrees and there's the steel in twenty minutes—ductile, tough, hard as if from an open hearth, and dumped out at a saving of $3.00 a ton or better. KE is building a 756,000-ingot-ton oxygen converter of this type for Jones & Laughlin.

If steel is the rose in Henry's lapel, aluminum is the diamond-studded tiara on his head. Before the war aluminum meant Aluminum Company of America. Today, while bigger than ever, Alcoa is only one of three U.S. giants, and Kaiser Aluminum and Chemical, with D. A. (Dusty, of course) Rhoades as its boss and twenty modern plants scattered across the country, supplies about one-fourth of the national need. That's four times more aluminum than the whole U.S. produced before World War II.

The bauxite comes from Jamaica, which long had wondered why its red soil wasn't fertile, and just before the war learned why—the island was a great blob of bauxite, the raw ore of aluminum. Kaiser Aluminum took an option on a choice segment of it, and in '51 Kaiser Engineers built a 13-mile railroad and handling facilities from the mine to the sea. The last mile of the railroad was down 500-foot cliffs and over earthquake faults. It was highballed through, and the infertile red clay now moves by ship for the Mississippi. It is refined at Baton Rouge and Gramercy, Louisiana, into alumina, and thence goes to reduction plants at Tacoma, Spokane, New Orleans, and Ravenswood, West Virginia. Of the New Orleans plant and its Aladdin-like story of creation, a description is elsewhere in these pages. After reduction to primary aluminum, the light silvery metal is shipped off to other fabricators or to Kaiser finishing mills in Washington, Ohio, Maryland, Indiana, and West Virginia.

Kaiser Aluminum & Chemical had its start in 1940 under the name Permanente Metals Corporation, which was producing magnesium under that title and building those one-a-day ships. It picked up three idle war-built aluminum plants in '46 and started ladling out that metal in increasing quantities until, with 1952–53, it became really burly by means of mighty new plants on the lower Mississippi.

Kaiser Aluminum & Chemical has over 15,000 stockholders and 17,000 workers, and it makes lots of money—$43,500,000 in the fiscal year 1955–56. The "& Chemical" produces basic refractory materials and chemicals for industry. The plants are at Natividad and Moss Landing, California, and Columbiana, Ohio; the raw material is a mountain of high-grade crystalline dolomite; and the other main ingredient is water from the Pacific, plus clever mechanical mass handling. Magnesia is the basic stuff of firebrick and the lining for cement kilns and steel furnaces that sizzle at 3,200 degrees F. And magnesia assists in the making of glass, ceramics, paper, sugar, drugs, petroleum, rayon, and rubber, and in helping things to grow on the farm.

With Kaiser Aluminum in the midst of a new $335 million expansion, Henry Kaiser said in '56, "Aluminum is only at the beginning. We know that U.S. aluminum production by 1965 once more must be at least doubled."

Kaiser Aluminum is presently (1957) engaged in a major construction program involving $300 million, two-thirds of which is represented by a fully integrated reduction plant and sheet and foil rolling mill at Ravenswood, West Virginia. Initial units went into production early in 1957 and when completed the Ravenswood plant will have an annual capacity of 125,000 tons of primary aluminum. Kaiser Aluminum will move its raw materials from mine to processing plant to fabricating plant along a direct all-water route terminating near the center of a market accounting for 70 per cent of United States aluminum consumption.

The erection of an enormous bubble of aluminum into a domelike auditorium, accomplished in Hawaii in twenty working hours, indicated that something new has been introduced as feasible for future public buildings, amusement centers, and supermarkets. The dome can cover 1,800 seated persons like a huge umbrella, yet has no interior supports of any kind. It was another Kaiser "first," and Henry enjoyed it.

Among the graver problems of this tormented world, India has been long with us—the country with too many people and too little everything else except death and poverty. A man of India saw what mining and manufacturing had done for Britain. He decided that his nation must industrialize. That would give employment, would produce material things, would chase the wolf from at least a few hundred thousand doors. He set up a cotton and weaving mill. It gave employment indeed; it provided wages; he sold it at a profit and built a new one. With air conditioning, reading rooms, recreation grounds, day nurseries, and slum clearance, he really made a stir. He built more mills, hydroelectric plants; hunted up deposits of iron, coal, and limestone; invited those of

India's 400 million who had any money to throw some of it in with him; with 8,000 native shareholders built a steel mill. That was in 1911. New enterprises were added—trucks and buses, locomotives, machine tools, farm tools, chemicals, soaps, oils, cement, hotels.

His name was Jamshedji Nusserwanji Tata, but he was beginning to look like a turbaned, slimmed-down Henry Kaiser. In the midst of plans for impressive expansion of his steel mill, the inspired man died. But his industrial republic was on a good foundation, his sons were able, and the plans for Tata Iron & Steel Co., Ltd., went ahead. Kaiser Engineers Division was called in.

India, shown the way to industrialization by the late J. N. Tata, and booted onward by its present government, was resolved to raise the national finished-steel output from 1,300,000 to 4,300,000 tons—and do it within five years. Russia had undertaken to build a big plant in India by 1959, the Germans by 1961. Tata currently produced 70 per cent of India's steel ingots. What could Kaiser offer in the matter of increasing the capacity of the Tata plant by 45 per cent?

The men who sat down with the Tatas were Henry J. and Edgar F. Kaiser and George Havas. They undertook to have the new $130 million plant up and its machinery whirring within thirty months. That would be by May 31, 1958.

The orders for blast furnace, open-hearth furnaces, blooming mill, structural mills, and continuous sheet bar mill, for coke ovens and sintering plant and the myriad things that make a modern steel works have been placed. The plant is rising. As so often in Kaiser history, the race is against time. Against Germany, as well. Above all, against Russia; the private-enterprise brand of get-it-done against the communistic. Kaiser's personnel chief in India, N. J. Lipner, starts

his business day at 7 A.M. A hundred American technicians
are on the ground wrestling with such problems as how
to protect the heads of turbaned workmen whose religion
prohibits steel helmets; how to get the stuff to Jamshedput,
150 miles west of Calcutta, on broken-down state-owned
railroads; and, later on, how to operate a modern mill, me-
chanically streamlined, without displacing labor. It all adds
up to a din of chuffing, unloading, pile driving, and hammer-
ing sufficient to send the tigers headlong for their jungles
and give new curl to the Sikh foremen's whiskers. As for the
Kaiser Engineers, every man on the job is as busy as a six-
armed Siva. But Henry knows that to India's millions, more
than the performance of his outfit is on trial. The Western
system is on trial.

Henry loves it.

Not the least of Kaiser's current responsibilities, and one
that strikes a dire note in the general paean, is an engineering
study on radioactive waste control undertaken for the U. S.
Navy. The study will deal with control and disposition of
liquid and gaseous effluents from research operations which
are scheduled by the Naval Radiological Defense Laboratory
in San Francisco. Meanwhile the Kaiser people, through
their Nuclear Engineering Division, design and construct the
Engineering Test Reactor for the Atomic Energy Commission
at Idaho Falls, Idaho.

Man has yet to learn whether he is building a bright new
Tomorrow, or has "had it."

Olof Erlander and his Tooe one day visited a Kaiser Foundation Hospital at the invitation of their youngest daughter,
Astrid, who had become a nurse. For twenty years now, ex-

cept for an interlude at shipbuilding, Olof had been one of the foremen on the eternal job of sandblasting and repainting the San Francisco-Oakland Bay Bridge. "When we finish this time, by yiminy, I retire," he'd told Tooe. "Sixteen million square feet of steel and 25 million rivets, that's too much to go over again, by yeese." Olof and Tooe's children were grown and scattered about the globe, and the couple had a snug orchard home over the Eastbay hills in Walnut Creek.

Astrid took them through the hospital. Everything is glass, air, sunshine, and convenience. She showed them the push-button beds, the self-serve appliances which adjust even the window drapes, the lavatory, radio, phonograph, and piped oxygen within reach of every bed. Private nurseries adjoin the maternity rooms. Mothers can reach from the bed to a bassinet drawer and take their babies in their arms at any time.

Tooe thought of the day in the early '30s, the Tar Town days, when her Trygvasson was born. In the windstorm that day, some of the roof had sheared off.

"It's different now, Olof, isn't it?" she said to her husband.

Olof nodded, and wondered what the man at the head of all this would be thinking up next. In that wondering he has company. The Kaiser top team—sons Edgar and Henry J. Kaiser, Jr., Trefethen, Rhoades, Ashby, Ordway, Clay Bedford, Marsh, Hackley, Marks, Reis, Olson, Barneyback, Harper, Burns, and Kaiser Engineers' Havas, Oppenheim, Price, Tim Bedford, Hallett, Larsen, Foster and Anderson—the men who must carry the ball—also wonder which way the boss will pass it next.

20

GET THROUGH AND GET ON

THE ESSENCE of heavy construction is time. The idea is to get the thing done, get it done well, and go on to the next job. Time is money. Time is overhead. A constructor may lose at least one tail of his shirt through a penalty clause if he fails to meet a completion date. But there's often a substantial bonus for beating the schedule.

For four major reasons, at least, the constructor moves his men and himself at jet clip:

Because it saves expense.

Because it beats weather to the punch.

Because it brings earlier return on the client's investment.

And because he's geared that way.

However, a constructor's natural desire to make time sometimes runs into obstacles not nature-made but man-made, or even woman-made.

As cat skinners found while readying the landscape for the dam and reservoir that will some day plug Karadj Canyon and provide clean water for Teheran, the teeming capital of Iran. When M-K's John Barry and his forces showed up in this seemingly barren gorge in the Elburz Mountains, they discovered that any number of native villages occupied the tiny bottoms and side gulches. Although the Plan Organization offered the villagers equitable settlement for their property and arranged to provide them with better lands, they were rooted by tradition to their ancestral farms. Barry's clanking dozers appeared and in one village the women swarmed out, pitched themselves to the ground, and for a short time really immobilized the works. The difficulty was quickly settled.

Owing to reasons beyond anyone's control, the Karadj Dam project still is stalled some years after the government of Iran issued its original letters of intent to M-K. However, the justification of the Karadj Dam as a water supply project has been reviewed and recommended by an international panel of noted engineers, and the dam will serve to provide ample water for unrestricted year-round supply to this oriental city of a million people.

Heavy construction is outdoor work. The one common ingredient of all outdoors, wherever located, is weather of one kind or another. Sometimes geography gives the job an extremely short working season, such as in a river canyon that is subject to seasonal floods. If the job can be brought up to a certain point, the knocking-off can be done without painful effects. But if the work isn't carried to that essential point, human life and all equipment may go down the wash in one tragic rush. There is only one way to beat that kind of nature. That is to plan every detail with care, get in there, get done, and get out. Fast.

Such a job was Box Canyon Dam on Pend Oreille River in the Pacific Northwest. By current standards this was no "biggie." The canyon is only 200 feet across and the plug was to be 120 feet high, containing a mere 29,000 yards of con-

crete. What made the job a speed job was the narrowness of
the gorge, the shortness of the working season, and the tan-
trums of the river. In the main it was a de-watering job, a
proposition of putting cofferdams down where deep water
rushed hell-for-lather, and then the immediate massing of
electric pumps to keep the bracketed area de-watered.

Bedrock was 145 feet down. Since there was no elbow room,
that represented too much overburden to excavate. So engineers had designed a vertical-arch "floating" dam, one that
would ride atop a foundation of sand and get its staying
power by pushing hard against abutments on both sides.

When Si Piedmont led his men into the gorge, in the spring
of '54, the river was 75 feet deep. Si is a disciple of the late
Woody Williams, whose jumbos outmatched the Colorado's
floods at Hoover. Si's problem was the same—to throw a dam
across a turbulent river before another spring could spread
his stuff from here to thataway. It was strictly a race against
the sweep hand of a watch, for the dam had to be topped out
and its massive gates installed before the next runoff could
swell the river to a roiling fury. Most of the concrete was
poured in the biting cold of winter. The work was complicated
by an existing Milwaukee Railroad trestle almost directly over
the damsite. The first task, to hew a diversion tunnel, send
the Pend Oreille surging through the detour above and below the damsite, had been done by previous contractors, who
had then decided that the dam could not be built.

The diversion, acknowledged by old dam hands to be unusually tricky, was finished early in August. A thundering
blast crumbled a concrete plug in the mouth of the diversion
tunnel, sending much of the river's flow through the bore and
around the damsite. The builders then pushed downstream

and upstream cofferdams across the Pend Oreille's channel to isolate the work area.

M-K's pumps and draglines moved in. By mid-October, concrete began to spill into place. Winter struck. Simon kept on working his men around the clock, seven days a week. As the dam reached upward, 40-foot sheet piling was driven to protect the sand foundation. A peak force of 600 men, working so close together that they practically had their arms in each others' mackinaws, somehow licked the gorge. Less than a year after the start, the 75-foot-high steel gates were swung into place. The message "Mission completed," or, perhaps, "There's your damn dam," sped to headquarters, just as Woody, Jack Bonny, and H.W. had known it would come.

An outlay of a million or multiple millions has a way of laying up heavy interest charges, and the owners of a tunnel, a pipeline, refinery, dam or powerhouse or canal like to see some offsetting revenue coming in. A tunnel to divert a river to make possible a dam to back the river up and lead it into penstocks is no revenue producer at all until the generators start whirring. So the contractor will bore his tunnel from both ends and also, if it's a big one, both ways from the middle, to save time and get done. Whatever he builds, it's the same situation in principle. Make speed!

In the northern bulge of Iraq is a region of flaming wells which King Nebuchadnezzar knew, and so did Biblical personages Shadrach, Meshech, and Abednego. In A.D. 1927 the "fiery furnace" region became the Kirkuk oil field, and a few years later its British developers, Iraq Petroleum Company, Ltd., ran its pair of pipelines from there to the Mediterranean. The lines forked, ending at Haifa and Tripoli. When fighting in Palestine sealed the Haifa branch, the London managers of Iraq Petroleum decided to lay another line, connecting

Kirkuk with the Syrian coast at Banias some 60 miles north of Tripoli. Steve Bechtel was invited to London to discuss the project, and he offered to build it provided he be permitted to shave half a year or so from the construction period estimated by the British. IPC wanted its new pipeline but found this type of prodding a bit disconcerting. But the Bechtel staff's studies had been so thorough that the San Franciscan's recommendations carried, and the Britons relaxed in the pleasant consciousness that such hustle would save them the interest on millions.

April '52 saw the line completed that six full months ahead of schedule, as promised. But something new had entered the world oil picture. Abadan, the major refinery of the Middle East and everywhere, was shut down by political difficulties in Iran. So Bechtel's self-applied discipline of no waste time proved valuable. The additional 300,000 barrels a day pouring into the free world's oil supply through Iraq pipeline, six months ahead of the owners' schedule, went a long way toward paying for the new project.

Perhaps he is born to hurry; perhaps he acquires the habit. Anyway, your international heavy constructor becomes a symbol of perpetual motion to his associates even when he is sitting still. H. W. Morrison's rush habits developed early, and if threescore years and ten have slowed him up in the slightest, nobody is able to get close enough to his coattails to discern it. He still logs a quarter-million miles a year, which is equal to the distance to the moon. Nothing disturbs such a traveler as much as a disrupted schedule. In 1954 he was in Ankara, Turkey, and ready to get out on a certain plane. The hour arrived, Harry and Ann grabbed their hand luggage, and were informed that bad weather ahead had canceled the flight. The fuming started. It was big smoke. H.W. declared he had to be in Adana that night, hired a car and driver, silenced his wife with "Ann, you must have learned by now that the Morrisons keep on schedule whether they travel the easy or the hard way," and set off on the 300-mile steep, crooked, narrow mountain drive. The Turk at the wheel knew no word of English. But he perceived that this man from America wanted speed. And the man from America got it. Ten hours later, after being well bounced between the top and the seat, the couple were in Adana. H.W. had kept to his schedule. His purpose, to have a look at his Seyhan Dam.

The irresistible timetable sometimes meets the immovable obstacle, however, with no respect for the titan who gets caught in between.

Steve Bechtel left Dhahran by private plane for Riyadh in the early days of his Middle East activities; he had an appointment with King Ibn Saud, the monarch of Saudi Arabia. It seemed worth while to break the journey and pay a brief call on an intervening emir or governor. Word to that effect, requesting forty-five minutes, had been sent ahead. The Bechtel plane came down on the desert, Steve and companions got out, a reception committee took them to the emir's pavilion, and they went in. The walls, in that dim interior, seemed to be lined with dark pilasters. The emir awaited at the far end of the shadowy room. As their eyes became adjusted, the Americans made a discovery. Those pilasters were men. Well, if their host wanted to use the local citizenry as decorations, it was all right with the visitors. Steve Bechtel did his best to produce the right salaam and, through an interpreter, wished his host the best of health and made known anew that, regrettably, he had only three-quarters of an hour to spend on this enjoyable visit. The local dignitary accepted all this, with an amendment. He informed Bechtel, "You will be here three days." "Three days!" exclaimed Bechtel. "I must be in Riyadh, the capital, at two o'clock." "You will be here three days," repeated the turbaned one.

Steve explained. He was a very busy man. His plane was ready to depart.

The emir informed, "I have sent your plane back to the seacoast."

About then the visitors perceived that the male figures around the walls were heavily armed with scimitars and fire-arms. These guards just stood there, exerting passive pressure. The Bechtel party stayed three days.

They were merry days, for the emir had invited everybody who was anybody to come and meet the noted engineer. At one o'clock on the third day Steve's plane returned for him. After ceremonious leave-taking, he went on. His associates re-call with chuckles that the head of their organization spent the rest of the summer trying to get himself back on schedule.

The rapidity with which American engineer-constructors can turn out a job of size is becoming legendary. The feat of Kaiser Engineers in the "Third Battle of New Orleans," a per-formance inspired by a national emergency, is a fair example. Late in 1950 the hydroelectric power resources of the Pacific Northwest were already inadequate for the nation's alumi-num requirements. Trouble with Russia seemed approaching a climax. A freeze-up along the Columbia would cut down on the production of aircraft and a thousand military items. Tele-phone wires brought the voice of Defense Mobilizer Charles E. Wilson to the Kaiser offices on the other side of the con-tinent. Henry J. whipped east to Washington. The problem was simple: America was confronted with one of the most deadly adversaries in the long history of would-be world con-querors. The country could deal with the Kremlin only from a platform of strength. Could Kaiser's forces add a hundred thousand tons a year to aluminum production, and if so, how soon? (One hundred thousand tons was more, perhaps, than all Russia was producing in a like time.)

Kaiser could. The industrialist found himself once more a constructor with a job to do—and to do fast. A lifelong habit of his, to shoot for the moon and let his cohorts worry about details, produced the answer instantly. The words "Design a four potline aluminum plant—location as yet undetermined" flashed to Kaiser's engineers in Oakland on November 9. George Havas, with his assistant general manager Lou Oppenheim; division manager E. C. Anderson; project engineers George Scheer, W. A. Voght; and construction manager Frank Backman sprang into a huddle. That night and thereafter lights burned late in Oakland. Calculations, estimates, and drawings tumbled out, followed by blueprints by the thousands.

The plant was on paper from the ground up before the ground itself had been decided upon. On February 9 the word came—Chalmette. That's down below New Orleans on the Mississippi mud, but it's handy by sea to the bauxite sources of Jamaica and the South American Guianas, and close to a fuel source.

Andy Jackson fought the British in the Pakenham Oaks of Chalmette in 1814 and made the Kentucky long rifle, the southern cotton bale, and the new American republic respected around the world. A second battle was fought nearby when Admiral Farragut ran the forts of the river and reduced the city of New Orleans in the Civil War. Now that mudbank was the scene of a third "battle."

Engineers probed, studied, and decided to drive a million feet of pilings. Water was hit a few feet down and part of the pile driving was directed by a deep-sea diver. Pumps and ditches fought the river to drain the sticky land. Subcontractors swarmed to the spot. On top of the piling and the foundations, 25,000 tons of steel rose. Swiftly they shaped up, aluminum-sheeted, into machine shops, warehouses, and housing for the potlines, which are tremendous rows of electric cookers, each pot more than 21 feet long, 11 feet wide, and 13 feet high, for production of nearly half a ton of aluminum to each pot a day. When the project reached its full stature, there were sixteen buildings housing these fireless cookers, each building 960 feet long and sheltering a line of seventy-two pots. The plant called for a constant flow of electric current equal to half of all that produced by Hoover Dam; but in this case gas-fueled engines would drive the generators. That was one reason why Chalmette had been chosen— Louisiana has natural gas.

The complicated organism rose in a thousand forms—a pumping station with a capacity of 195 million gallons a day, which was twice the water needed by New Orleans itself; shipping facilities to handle the raw material which would first go upriver to Baton Rouge to be refined to alumina, and returned downriver to Chalmette; facilities for the coke, pitch, cryolite, aluminum fluoride, and coal which an aluminum plant ingests; a carbon paste plant for mixing the coke and tar that would provide the anodes and line the pots; and sixteen turbogenerators cracking out 478,000 kilowatts. For here was to be the daddy of aluminum reduction plants in this country.

Yet in the midst of the hurly-burly, time was found for sentiment. The Pakenham Oaks, where Old Hickory made history and the British general was killed, were squarely where a warehouse was to go. The oaks still stand; the warehouse went elsewhere.

To design all this, find the materials for it, get it made, gather it, and put it together was an undertaking before which the mind of the layman grows dizzy. But Henry had promised it, and he not only fulfilled the pledge, but doubled it. The planned capacity of the plant, originally set for 100,-000 tons annually, had been stepped up to 200,000. On December 11, 1951, ten months and a day after the assignment had been accepted, the plant on Chalmette battlefield was delivering its first big pour.

They gave "Electric Charley" Wilson a luncheon that day in the ballroom of a New Orleans hotel. He said, "I wish Joseph Stalin were here." He added a story. Some of Kaiser's lieutenants had demurred when the boss had undertaken to put that second 100,000-ton capacity together concurrently with the first. They said, taken aback, "Now wait a minute. Just a minute. Rome wasn't built in a day."

"We weren't running that job," retorted Henry J.

21

THE SECRET WEAPON—
RESOURCEFULNESS

DOWN in Sonora, Mexico, where Mocuzari Dam was rising, a tire maintenance superintendent named Stu Compton scratched his head and pondered what to do about repairing the abraded walls of truck tires without dismounting or deflating them. Such tires stand almost as high as a man. Then Stu was clouted by an idea. He sank a heavy steel beam vertically into concrete, ran the next ailing tire up alongside it, placed a screw-type jack horizontally against the steel post for anchorage, and inserted an electric tire-patching hotplate between jack and the damaged portion of the tire. The resulting patch was something to admire, and how much time Stu's invention has saved his boss whose big trucks number hundreds, and how much weight of rubber and air doesn't have to be lifted any more, are for the slide-rule boys to figure. Stu just smiles and waves his limping trucks up to the anchor post, unless he is now a big boss somewhere, solving bigger problems.

During the erection of the C. J. Strike Dam on the Snake River in southwestern Idaho, a group of supervisors went into a huddle and came out with a new method, fast and thrifty, for handling sacked cement. They combined two circular saws, a short conveyor belt and part of a potato digger and there was a machine that ripped the sack, dumped it, shook it clean, and tossed it into an incinerator in one quarter the time required by hand methods. H. W. Morrison, admiring, calls that "Em-Kayingenuity." Competitors called it smart.

In 1957 Morrison "Em-Kayingenuity" had another work-out, at Elmendorf Air Force Base near Anchorage, Alaska. Because the outside temperature was a lusty 32 degrees below zero and fresh plaster was giving off moisture inside the new barracks and condensing and freezing on windows and walls in half-inch-thick sheets, project superintendent Mel Evenson hollered to Seattle for 200 electric fans on a rush order and hitched them up for a big blow. The humid air was then hurled out of the $4 million project by means of fans placed in old five-gallon paint cans from which the bottoms had been cut. In twenty-four hours the interior was as dry as Sahara and the barracks were headed for completion five months ahead of schedule.

Big boss, walking boss, or plain construction stiff—ideas don't care which one they hit. Says Morrison, "The business of large-scale, heavy construction contracting is a distinctive one, requiring an exceptionally high degree of sustained energy and resourcefulness."

When a man is turned loose with a million dollars' worth of equipment, a set of blueprints, and a schedule, in some spot which nature seems to have designed to be inaccessible, this man is expected to do his job and thrive on whatever is unusual. What he isn't expected to do is rush home and ask for directions. Some of the ways in which he meets his issues, little or big, are touched with audacity and sometimes with genius. The whole construction industry chuckled with ap-

Hungry Horse, 3,100,000 yards of concrete, world's fourth for size.
Below, how they direct highline landings during concrete pouring.

Venezuelans take to "dinamita" and hard hats.

Pakistani tackle Sui Gas Line under M-K bosses.

Local talent: above, a Saudi Arab tames an iron horse; below, Afghans tamp for Arghandab Dam.

Sons of Peru help turn a river.

Jungle tunneling, above, and mountain splitting, below—in Brazil.

Arabs and an air drill prepare a shot in the Nejd.

Highballing on a highline at Hungry Horse.

preciation when it heard about a piece of heavy machinery that was landed on a mid-Pacific isle to be placed in a concrete pit, ready and waiting—with no jack shipped along with the machinery to sustain and ease the load downward. Someone with an eye for the practical filled the pit with ice cubes. The heavy chunk of machinery was slid out on the cubes, they melted, and there was the generator or whatnot, lowered by the tropic sun to exactly where wanted.

Arizona, which admits that certain stretches of its broad terrain have been desert in their day, is rapidly turning—in parts—into a garden under the hand of the Reclamation people as they strew government canals hither and yon. One of these ditches, known as the Wellton-Mohawk division of the Gila project, drives for 50 miles along the rambling bed of the Gila River, which is now dry save in flood time. Project manager Jim Ricker found that he had to have special equipment to shove all those yards of gravel out of the way and leave a slot of exact grade and contour.

With white-polled excavation superintendent Bud Snowball standing beside him and exhorting him to think of something to make the job go faster, he and the only snowball in the Gila Valley solved the problem. Ricker took a conventional wheel-type trench digger and had wide side-cutting prism wings built onto it. As it chugged down the valley it resembled a Sierra flange-type railroad snowplow. Where this "Rickerwagon" passed, a perfect trench lay open to the sun, everything true and beveled. The practical value of this machine was that it made it economical to build countless miles of standard 2-foot-bottom laterals previously done by slower methods. Behind the trencher came special equipment that applied a concrete lining. A "tugger," straddling the canal subgrade behind the trencher, pulled a slip-form by cable.

The slip-form, riding the new canal bed, was fed concrete by a mobile mixing machine and a crane traveling together up on the rim of the ditch. This bunch of gimmicks skimmed across lots at a clip of 2,600 feet of canal a day, all dug and concreted.

So far as the record shows, the hard-hat boys of M-K haven't built any ice-block igloos in quantity yet, though they probably could show the Eskimos some tricks as well as learn a few. Meanwhile they've developed a method of running up concrete igloos. The job, at Fort Richardson, Anchorage, Alaska, was to toss up thirty-nine buildings shaped like Quonset huts, 26 by 60 feet, to house ammunition. A. W. Erickson, Alaska district manager, and Walter Harfst, building construction manager, proceeded to show their boss why they felt that a bid 20 per cent below the nearest competitor's might be a money-maker after all. They dispensed with the central casting yard and the elaborate forms indicated for semicircular concrete pouring, and broke the job down into six slightly curving panels for each igloo. These 16-ton sections were cast, each on the slab floor of its intended hut; tilted up into position by a crane; and hooked together and cemented. The job was done in four months instead of eight, and Aner and Walter, grinning widely, were ready to take on the next one.

At Hoover Dam, Henry Kaiser's Tom Price had the whole enormous aggregate and cement-mixing plant working by push-button, one man doing the pushing. Kaiser found another answer to a materials-handling problem when Shasta Dam went up in the 1940s.

The poser was to get 10 million tons of sand and gravel across 9.6 miles of mountaintop and valley and plunging river without paying the Southern Pacific railroad what looked like a fancy price. (The railroad had just moved many miles of its main track to make way for the dam and would have enjoyed getting its money back.) The answer to this high freight rate, so noble from the railroad's viewpoint and so heathenish from Kaiser's, was a "rubber railroad"—a transmission belt just twice 9.6 miles in length, since it went both ways. Operating with twenty-six transfer points that handed the cobbles and fine stuff over from hilltop to hilltop, the belt was a grand success, clipping 7 cents a ton-mile from the railroad's price.

Belt conveyors aren't new, and Kaiser's solution in this case was simply in the magnitude of the thing and the rugged terrain involved. For generations bucket and screw conveyors, followed by belts, had been used in grist mills and on heavy rollers in foundries and auto plants. Today coal moves by belt for 103 miles across Ohio River country and 5 million tons of aggregate traveled 7 miles at the building of Bull Shoals Dam in Arkansas. Since belts can climb 32 per cent grades and hang onto their loads—trucks quitting at 10 per cent; since they equalize grades and smooth everything out, new uses are continually being proposed for them, whether to move Texas wheat across Texas miles—the state having much of both—or the dream of transporting New York City folks by means of moving sidewalks, perhaps some day taking them all the way home to Suburbia.

When concrete cures after being poured, it heats up—a chemical process called heat of hydration. The heat would fissure a big dam and fill it with leaks were it not controlled. At Hoover Dam an ingenious way of meeting the problem, which was acute because of the size of the concrete mass, was developed by Professor W. F. Durand of Stanford University. (That was over a quarter of a century ago. Now past ninety years of age, Professor Durand still is going strong.) He suggested threading the dam with a grid of pipes carrying moving water. The pipes, after serving their prime purpose, are still in the dam for reinforcement.

The cooling down of concrete is a permanent problem for contractors and they allow for its expense when they enter a bid. When bids were opened for Table Rock Dam on the White River in Missouri, the winners were those old allies and joint venturers, Morrison-Knudsen and Utah Construction. And when the first 8-yard bucketful of the million and a quarter yards of concrete was reeled downward from a cableway in 1955, it came from a multimillion-dollar concrete manufacturing plant that had treated the ponderous stuff as if it were so much ice cream. The crushed rock had been pre-cooled by chill air drawn by fans over refrigerated coils. Then the rock had been dropped into storage bins and there kept under arctic temperatures just like frozen peas in a supermarket. When the aggregate came out of the bins to be mixed with cement, ice-making machines got into the act by producing flaked ice to go into the mixing water. The resulting concrete started its career 35 degrees cooler than if left to nature.

James P. Growden, tunnel expert, on loan from the Aluminum Company of America as consultant for certain critical war work in Hawaii, is credited with one of the magical ideas which helped to make America strong. All Jim Growden did, basically, was turn a blueprint sideways and look at it from the new angle. Out of that came a saving of months of time and perhaps thousands of lives.

The scene was Oahu, the year 1940, the bombs from Japanese planes not yet fallen on Pearl Harbor. But the Navy's braid in charge of docks and harbors was looking ahead, thoroughly scared. It knew that if bombs did fall, the Navy's fuel in exposed tanks would be doomed. It wanted Red Hill, behind Pearl, hollowed out and underground storage vaults put in there. The tanks would essentially be a set of steel and concrete-lined tunnels. To hollow out the mountain would be a routine job of drilling, blasting, and mucking—the debris, as it was loosened, to be power-shoveled into trucks and hauled out. Growden, puffing on a cigar thoughtfully, yanked those blueprints around and said, "Why not stand the bins on end?" Oil in storage doesn't care whether it's lying down or standing up. He began to sketch them out—round-ended bins, each as high as a twenty-story building, which could be hewed out by working downward from the top of the mountain through a series of vertical shafts, with a small horizontal tunnel at the bottom to receive the loose stuff and carry it out on an endless belt. Easier to throw loose rock down a hole, Jim reasoned, than lift it piecemeal into trucks which have to back and turn and squirm.

Since there are twenty such cisterns, each holding 60,000 tons of oil, there was plenty of rock to handle and Jim Growden's notion was deemed real bright. So it was done, $41 million worth of work that might have cost far, far more. The storage vaults are still there, below the penetration radius of any conventional bomb, holding their contents in standing position and no objections heard. The vaults will go on doing their job in the silence and darkness of Red Hill until atomic fuel fully replaces petroleum.

22

GAMBLES THAT PAID OFF

IN IDAHO near the Canadian border, a group of onlookers stood nervously in the summer breeze while a powderman made some final arrangements. The place was Cabinet Gorge on deep, swirling Clark Fork River where a structure was about to be erected that has come to be called The Dam That Couldn't Wait.

Cabinet Gorge is a slash in the Bitterroot Range where the river, a headwater branch of the Columbia, hurtles along at a normal depth of 80 feet. In times of flood, and floods can stab like lightning, the flow of 12,000 cubic feet a second has been known to multiply itself by ten. Where it hits Cabinet Gorge, the water makes a swift Z-turn. The Washington Water Power Company of Spokane had decided it wanted a dam in that spot and wanted it fast, and any engineer who looked down into Cabinet Gorge knew he had a problem on his hands. To drop a dam into that slot *might* be done in three years, if the floods didn't carry it away. But the power company craved to have at least one of its four 50,000-kilowatt generators humming within twenty-four months.

Woody Williams, in charge of management assignments in

the Boise area, had reached into M-K's bag of manpower and sent soft-spoken, hard-driving Harold E. Buckert to generally superintend the project (Buck had become a dam builder on Hoover twenty-two years before); John R. Barry as administrative manager; and Fred Reif as project engineer. The dam was to be 600 feet long and 208 feet high, of concrete, with a variable-center arch that would curve its back against the stream in a rarely beautiful setting—if it ever got there. There'd be the usual excavating; two 29-foot diversion tunnels; a 9-foot tunnel for ice diversion. There would also, as matters turned out, be a maximum river flow of 113,000 cubic feet a second come May 26, 1951, and 83,000 cubic feet a second on May 22, 1952. Those dates will live long in the memories of men who were down there. The engineers had watched in awe when the '51 flood went by. Somehow, equipment was retrieved. But when the work would be another year along, such a volume of water would have to be taken into account or the consequences would be completely disastrous.

It all came down to this: The river would have to be turned many months before the next May onslaught.

The tunnels were driven during the summer of 1951. By August everything was ready to kick the river, then in normal summer flow, through the two undermountain tubes. With the river turned, the dam erectors would have nine months to sling the dam itself in place.

So what was going to happen now, on this B day of August 22, 1951—B for Boom—was to be a supreme effort to lift the entire cliff on one side of Clark's Fork River and lay it over in the hole, 450 feet deep. A $40 million dam and power development depended upon the outcome. If that cliff could be flung outward in one grand clap, and laid where wanted, the

river would be forced into its underground detours, and work
below the barrier could go ahead.

A hundred and ten thousand pounds of dynamite had been
coyote-holed into place. As ably as men can aim a charge
of that kind, the "gun" was trained. Everybody knew that the
aim was right. But did the cliff know it?

The powderman squatted to his box and shoved the lever
forward.

Like a tired old hen humping to let her chicks out from
under her feathers, the cliff, 30,000 cubic yards of it, rose and
released its brood. The rock scurried outward and flumped
into the gorge, and the din rattled about in that tight zigzag
canyon. The river dashed against a brand-new barrier, slid
alongside it, found the tunnels, poured through—and the
shovels hurried down to scoop and lift.

What happened after that was plain around-the-clock
work, while a necklace of concrete was hung around the
throat of Clark's Fork. The necklace was well-bediamonded
with ice before winter got through with it. In the following
May, when the Bitterroots let go with all they had and the
cresting flood came down with destruction in its fists, the dam
was there, its half circle of artificial stone taking the smash
and transferring it harmlessly to the canyon walls. Eighteen
months from the start of work, the power from a 126-foot head
of water began flowing across Idaho to Spokane, Washington.

The little dam that was born of a big gamble is a thing of
beauty—slim, narrow-hipped, only 40 feet thick at the base,
containing a mere 126,000 cubic yards of concrete; drawing
its great strength from its deep curve against the stream. It
is a true arch making almost a half circle across the canyon.
It sings a song of power as four 50,000-kilowatt generators
whirl their well-oiled course. But construction engineers still

wake in the night and wonder: What if the cliff had gone some other way?

Hal Buckert and John Barry hardly had time to go home and get a haircut before they were on their way again—Buckert to build Seyhan Dam in Turkey and Barry to manage irrigation, drinking water, and sanitation plans for Iran.

Sometimes a bet pays off. And sometimes it doesn't. When Comstock Midwestern was building the western two-thirds of Trans Mountain pipeline, a reef of rock was struck in Coachella Canyon that parallels the Canadian Pacific tracks on the uphill side. The canyon is narrow, with a mad stream below and steep slopes springing for the summits. To find room for the pipeline, it was necessary to climb up at one point, burrow under the railroad tracks, make a sharp bend, and return downward under the tracks again. But there was that reef. If it could be moved in a hurry there would be no delay to the trains. So a powder expert allowed as he would try. He was given a powder maximum and told to go ahead. But the expert wanted to make sure. On his own responsibility he doubled the charge and let 'er go. The reef moved, all right, but so did the Canadian Pacific Railroad—20 feet. Fired for exceeding his authority, the powder monkey was heard in a barroom, moaning into his whisky, "If it had worked I'd 'a' been a hero. Instead, I'm a bum."

Each job has its moments when everything hangs in the balance—success or failure, profit or loss, enhanced reputation or everything-gone-to-pot. As Harry Morrison puts it, "This is not a type of business that permits you to relax."

Bechtel's forces and subcontractors faced one of those moments while crossing Niagara River with a pair of 20-inch

pipelines in the fall of '54. The immediate 80-mile section was
to be a link in the 2,200-mile system of Trans-Canada Pipe
Lines Limited, bringing natural gas from Alberta to Ontario
and Quebec.

The point where the river was to be crossed is a 2,000-foot
raceway, 9 miles below Niagara Falls. There was no great
rush about that part of it, so the boys took nine hours. The
pipes, welded into long sections and well weighted, were
lugged by sideboom tractors and simultaneously dragged by
cables, and they went across as neatly as ever the acrobat
Blondin once tightroped his way over the falls themselves,
pausing to eat a banana while on his way. But when Bechtel's people reached the 300-foot Welland Canal beyond the
river, urgency entered the picture. The canal is a busy place
for commercial shipping. Some thirty vessels a day use it. As
a ship is annoyed to find a pipeline looming like a sea serpent
across its bow, traffic was notified to hold up for two hours
while the pipeliners dragged their 417-foot string across, sub-
merged it, and got the hell out of there. With concrete weights
of about a ton apiece holding the pipe down at 18-foot intervals, and a drum winch pulling, the long steel hose was
snaked across in less than an hour and everybody's reputation was made, for this time anyway.

Though, had they been sailors, the pipeliners would have
discovered that they didn't need to rush so hard. A high wind
had immobilized all the vessels that were waiting, and the
ships couldn't have proceeded anyway.

The two big financial gambles of heavy contracting are at
the bidding and at that point on the job when the winner
learns whether he has made money or lost it. The excitement
grows high as "letting" day approaches and, in hotel rooms

and on trains and planes, bidders go over and over their figures, adding here, subtracting there, and often letting hunch affect their final proposals as they try to read the opposition's minds. When Hoover Dam was bid for by the Six Companies, each associate figured it his own way and then the figures were averaged. The $5 million that they left on the table was a headache that had them all throbbing, and only superlative management brought the gamble off. The reverse of that was in 1955 when Morrison won a pair of dams in the California Sierra with a $31 million bid that was only $17,000 under the opposition—scarcely the price of the mustard that would go on the ham sandwiches.

Following Hoover, the Six Companies jointly took on the job of raising the height of San Francisco's O'Shaughnessy Dam in Yosemite National Park. During this work Felix Kahn, the group's financial wizard, worried himself sick about the slice Uncle Sam would want to annex for income tax. But it all came out happily, for the Six lost $800,000 on their deal, and at a directors' meeting they jibed, "Well, Felix, we fixed the tax situation up for you."

Frank Crowe was a close figurer and he went over the Six Companies' estimates for Shasta Dam and declared them too low by about a third of a million. So the bid was raised. But rival contractors got the job by just about that third of a million. Crowe's educated guesswork was seldom on the losing side, but it had been that time. But the winning bidders, forgiving everything, hired Crowe to raise the structure for them, and he did it with notable style.

His old employers also continued to use Frank's long head when a bidding came up. In 1946, M-K put him on figuring Kortes Dam on the North Platte in Wyoming. Shortly after, at the age of sixty-three, Crowe's heart stopped beating. Two weeks later the Kortes bids were opened. Crowe's figure was lowest. On his last shot the "Old Man" had been again the winner.

Confidence and nerve are as much a part of a constructor's equipment as long-armed power shovels and cranes. Henry Kaiser likes to tell of a couple of instances when courage was about all there was to pit against natural adversaries of a formidable kind. Of the Bonneville Dam in the lower Columbia River, "We were warned that the raging waters would rise twenty to thirty feet in a day or two, ripping to shreds any puny works of man. The native Indians had a legend that no man would ever walk across the Columbia. Government engineers were doubtful that it could be done. The bonding companies refused to take the risk of the hazardous project. Later, when our young men had built the dam that had been declared impossible, an official said, 'The kids succeeded because they never had been licked.' They had no fear of failure."

In 1940, when Britain was desperate for ships, a group of English purchasing commissioners journeyed across the United States to talk about thirty vessels which they understood a party named Kaiser would undertake. They asked for a look at his shipyards. He took them to a mudflat across the bay from San Francisco and said "Here they are." He explained: "It's true you see nothing but mud here. But it's space —space for thousands of workers to come together, build homes, park their cars, and mass their materials. Just envisage the yard that can be built in a matter of months to pour out ships." It was a hard bit of visualization, but the visitors took the gamble with Henry. The result, before the din died down, was not one shipyard but seven, not just thirty ships but about fifteen hundred.

Harry Morrison, the cautious but not too cautious, puts it, "You have to ask yourself, 'How much can I afford to lose?' and let that be your limit." About like the fellow who approached the Las Vegas roulette wheel, muttering wistfully, "I hope I break even tonight. I need the money."

Construction achievements all over the map haven't been performed through any inherent reluctance to buck the tiger, whether in the form of making a bid or of packing a mountain with dynamite and letting 'er go.

A contractor is a contractor for just one reason. It's because he's a born gambler, and can't help it.

23

HERE COME THE ELEPHANTS

ONCE there were the shovel and the wheelbarrow. Then somebody invented the scraper. It was a three-sided basin open at the front, with hardwood handles and a swivel hitch. It held from a quarter to half a yard, was drawn by animal power, and could be bought from the local blacksmith for about $4 or a couple of fat shoats. Later on, somebody with a bigger-and-better complex invented the Fresno scraper. Its improvements included a longer lip for shoving into the dirt and a lever or Johnson bar for heaving it over. With a span of mules ahead and the lines around his neck and over one shoulder, the driver could scoop new quantities up to the pile, where a half-dozen hand-shovelers, swinging rhythmically, tossed the dirt into a cart that was dumped somewhere by pulling the 2 by 4-inch planks out from the bottom. Around and around went the scraper, scooping, moving, piling as the driver somersaulted his rig with a flip. Plenty of sweat and grunting produced a lively scene. Came bigger Fresnos until an extra man was required to flip them, and the number of animals out ahead was whatever the skill of the driver permitted. Until petroleum as a power-fuel came along to dispute with hay, the Fresno was supreme in the western scene, and was reaching east.

It's different today.

Consider those gimmicks known as self-propelled carrying scrapers. On a representative job they double as power shovel and truck, excavating as well as hauling. Pulled by their own rubber-tired tractors, they scrape, gulp, and waddle off; disgorge and return for more. And a hill drops, and a valley rises.

Where the going is rough, drilling crews move their chattering wagon drills ahead, sinking holes for the blasting crews. Up soars the rock, and heavy-boomed power shovels and end-dump diesel trucks move in. Along easier stretches, where there's only dirt to move, the self-propelled scrapers and spreads of tractor-scraper combinations gouge and snort and waddle. Sometimes a "Siamese" tractor—two engines side by side in one chassis with one operator—pulls a "ripper," which is a tool designed to do just that. It weighs a dozen tons, and when it passes, mother earth knows that something is up there on her neck.

In the middle 1920s the oxyacetylene cutting and welding of steel came into general use. It opened up a new way of doing things with steel. One man thought he could build his own machines by this method, and he did. He was an inventor and a preacher, living at Stockton, California. His name was Robert G. LeTourneau. He became a pioneer in moving dirt with combination loaders and haulers, using the new tractors that were beginning to be so successful. He built the highway from Boulder City down to the damsite before the Six Companies got to work on the job. Bob LeTourneau invented machines that today are the backbone of dirt-moving methods. His was the forerunner of many successful

companies which have made fortunes with this type of equipment.

Henry Kaiser first saw Bob LeTourneau and his machines
working on a road job near Hayward, California. Not many
days passed before LeTourneau sold Kaiser his patents, and
was at work for Henry as master mechanic. They performed
several jobs together, and put up a factory at the Livermore
sand and gravel plant to build the "earth movers," as the machines were called. Later Kaiser sold the patents back to Le-
Tourneau at the same price he had paid for them. The two
men remained life-long friends, each going at the earth-
changing job in his own special way.

The power of a crawler-type tractor to go where it has a
mind to go, and carry its load along with it, was shown in
the job of tearing loose an icebound diesel locomotive for the
Southern Pacific in '52. The locomotive belonged to a train
that had been marooned in the snows of the Sierra Nevada
for three days. After the passengers were rescued by sled, the
budging of the frozen-in locomotive began, and it was accomplished by the sudden application of the engine's own
power plus that of the two D-8's, swung out ahead in tandem.
The ice released the locomotive with a shriek.

The use of two rigs when one could serve is ever an un-
pleasant sight to a contractor. It calls for the employment
of an extra man who must have pay, meals, a bed, social se-
curity, and one more construction camp movie seat or billiard
cue to keep him happy, also one-thousandth part of an extra
office manager, bookkeeper, secretary, and vice-president
somewhere as so much more overhead. These and other
considerations led M-K to place with Caterpillar an order for
the first ten D-9's ever delivered—tractors with dozer blades
14 feet long and 5 feet high. Said a job manager happily

when he saw them nudging hills around, "How those dirt-disturbers disturb dirt!"

When your heavy constructor tackles a major railroad grading job, a herd of mechanical elephants really shambles up and puts its shoulders to the work. Self-propelled carrying scrapers carve, haul off, and dump 23 cubic yards at a time. Twenty-three yards amount to a pile of earth 9 feet by 12 and 6 feet high around all four sides. The Model B Tournapull carries that much in one trip, without sideboards. If this seems sizable, Bucyrus-Erie makes it known that it has a 60-yarder on the drawing boards. The very large carriers are more profitably used in strip mining than on construction jobs.

Back in 1930–35 the 4-yard shovel was the largest generally used by contractors, although draglines up to 15 yards' capacity were also *de rigueur*. Now the 6-yard shovel is in there biting and champing, and some contractors use 10-yarders. (In mines the shovels are up to 35 yards.) On construction of the Missouri River dams the 10-yard shovel, on double crawlers, gnaws, lifts, and dumps a bite every twenty-two seconds.

When the Sante Fe railroad undertook to build 49 miles of new main line in Texas in 1955, M-K and a sponsoring co-venturer, H. B. Zachry Co., put eight spreads on the job and these proceeded to move a lot of Texas out of the way in a typical Texas dust-flurry. With thirty-three self-propelled carrying scrapers and thirty-two tractors doing the drudgery, the construction army highballed through between midsummer and late fall. All in order that passengers could get to Galveston or Chicago a trifle quicker and the hell with Fort Worth.

Cranes are growing bigger, too. One used on Chief Joseph Dam on the Columbia was a Monighan 450-W, a house-sized rig that usually "walks" on pontoonlike feet when going about its customary business as a dragline on excavation work. But here it was, resting on an electric-driven undercarriage that inched it along on rails, its 205-foot boom plucking buckets of concrete from railroad cars and swinging them out and dumping them into the intake structure. Old Chief Joseph, the Nez Percé Indian who fought the white man to a standstill with arrows, rocks, and carbines three-quarters of a century ago, would not be the only one to stare if he were to see this juggernaut at work. The paleface stares too.

Incidentally that husky machine was only one of a line of weight-lifters that keep growing bigger. Its antecedent was Bucyrus-Erie's 9-W Monighan with 30-foot tub (the circular base the rig rests on), but M-K wanted something with more power and a larger base. The result was a dirt-grabber known as 9-W Special, with 36-foot base, which became the standard production machine numbered 450-W. Its successor, 480-W, costing $550,000 at the factory and some $100,000 more for shipping and setting up on a western job, requires 4,000 man-hours for its erection.

Grand Coulee, that man-made mountain range of concrete, was put together with the aid of some tools really high and wide. These were two 270-ton cranes with booms longer than a football field, which moved along on a trestle and dumped those 10,500,000 yards of liquid rock.

Around the Grand Coulee, where work still goes on and will be going on for a long time, everything is of such a scale that even the language adjusts to a new set of standards. As, for instance, when the Reclamation people ordered the "armoring" of the bank of the river, in 1950, a short distance below the dam. It was a rock-dumping job but the rocks desired were such that one-ton chunks became known as "pebbles." A "rock" had to be from three tons up, and there were 294,000 tons of them, together with several hundred thousand tons of riprapping. To put the 800,000 tons of pebbles and rocks along the west bank, the rock-wrestlers arrived with trucks that really were trucks, hauled the material from a quarry, and laid it in place with a Manitowoc 4500 crane that operated a four-pronged grab hook on a 120-foot boom. "Here's one for your rock garden," the operator of the crane would call as he scooped up a chunk of 20 or so tons and laid it neatly in place.

Man has been building breakwaters against the waves for a long time, from the days of Rhodes and Carthage, at least. But when the job was undertaken of pushing back the breaking seas at Crescent City, California, Macco Corp. sent a Manitowoc to swing the cobbles. They fixed the crane up right fancy. With a radio phone around his neck, operator Leroy Smith kept in touch with the quarry, five miles away, and specified just the size of rocks he wanted for each load. And when Kaiser forces built the Long Beach breakwater, they tried something really eye-catching. They built huge barges, loaded them, towed them out, and dumped them by hauling them up on their beam-ends with cables and winches. A sea-going barge r'aring up like that, and letting go its tons of rock, gave the appearance of rough seas out in Santa Catalina Channel.

The enterprising highway-making tools known as paving machines operate on widely spaced tracks. When they have passed, a concrete strip is there that makes Rome's Appian Way look like a cowpath. This instrument is the ultimate expression (for the present) of the old-fashioned cement man's hand trowel, or grandma's sadiron, but it is one that the operator rides in style, and when it has made one pass, the whole scene is changed. In one June day at Portsmouth, New Hampshire, where an air force base was being built, two such machines belonging to M-K and Landers & Griffin placed 3,726 yards of concrete in two eight-hour shifts. With the help of such rigs, preceded and followed by other mechanical elephants and whales, the builders laid 12 million square feet of parking apron and a runway 11,620 feet long and 300 feet wide for the benefit of intercontinental bombers that had to get up fast into the stratosphere.

When it comes to road cargoes, Bechtel took a championship with the trundling of a record load for California's groaning highways—a stator for a steam electric plant being erected on California's Morro Bay. The "thing" weighed 224 tons. It was a cylindrical shape, 29 feet long and 12 feet high. Getting the stator from General Electric's plant at Schenectady had required a special railroad car with eight axles and sixteen wheels, and a special transcontinental routing to avoid tunnels.

For its last few miles a trucking subcontractor detailed sixty men. The load required 89 truck and dolly wheels with pneumatic tires, a 200-horsepower truck-tractor, and three helping truck-tractors to get it along the highway. It also took a sheaf of permits and a squad of cops. The trucking distance was less than 10 miles, most of it on a state highway, but the job stretched on for eight days, twenty-four hours a day. To safeguard the highway, the route was covered with 3-inch planks. The planks were laid 600 feet at a time, then picked up and carried forward. At points there were upgrades ranging to 10 per cent and downgrades up to 20 per cent. On the upgrades the three helper tractors lurched and strained, and on the down runs they held everything back with winches.

On the other side of the earth Bechtel men undertook to off-load, transfer, and erect a monumental high-octane unit for the refinery at Ras Tanura, Saudi Arabia, which had been carried half around the globe to the Persian Gulf, on one of the few ships with booms heavy enough to handle such a weight. There the 200-ton item, 13 feet in diameter and 80 feet long, was lowered into the sea at shipside and wheels were affixed while the monster was in the water. It was rolled over, hauled ashore by tugboat, pulled up on the sandy beach by three tractors, and hustled 7 miles down the road to its destination, where a mighty derrick hoisted it into place.

Bigness seems to seize the imagination of constructors as well as laymen. As stable a citizen as Frank Crowe was so carried away by the beauty of brute magnitude when he built Shasta Dam that he induced the Reclamation engineers to add 2 feet to its planned foundations just to make the total height of the structure 602 feet. "Some scissorbill will come along later and build another dam around six hundred feet high," he said, "and I want to push this one up above that round figure."

So, in the pursuit of size—big dams, big pipelines, big everything—we see 16-ton compactors with giant roller wheels faced with staggered rows of heavy steel pads, crunching about on off-highway jobs and pressing down the earth to support earth-moving equipment; we see trucks, scrapers, shovels, graders, loaders, and new monsters still without name.

When an experimental model of the D-9 Caterpillar was put up against another dozer, up to then considered big, and the drivers of the two rigs pulled in their clutches in a test of strength, the D-9 took the other machine straight back while the beaten machine's tracks churned forward. That was enough. The new elephant was king of the herd. For a few months, anyway.

Embedded in all this industrial history-making is, of course, the diesel engine. It operates compressors, asphalt plants, concrete carriers, and cranes; it crushes rock, makes ditch, dredges, excavates, and grades; it hoists, loads, pulls, paves, pumps, rolls, plows snow, powers tractors, shoves trucks, and is the steel-muscled mule of the game. Along with it have come the track that lays itself and picks itself up, and the tire that stands higher than a standing man's hat.

Big and fast and able as equipment becomes, the men do show up who can be readily taught to handle it. They show up both here at home, and at the far ends of the earth.

24

TEACHING—AND LEARNING—
IN FOREIGN LANDS

ON THE SANDS of Arabia a true believer got down from his yellow Tournapull, eyed the sun, determined the position of Mecca, and laid down his prayer rug and knelt. A long line of road machinery halted behind him and its drivers did the same. An American supervisor waited patiently, though wondering why all five prayers a day had to come on the boss's time.

The international constructor and his representatives, from gear-twisters to managers, are careful to respect ancient ways.

Except for key men—executives, engineers, and skilled equipment and maintenance men who can train others—the battalions that toil on dam, canal, highway, pipeline, or refinery are the sons of mountain, jungle, and desert who happen to be handy.

Erstwhile headhunters of New Guinea, Eskimo walrus fishers, and Afghan donkey herders operate bulldozers and usually make a good job of it. Along the high spine of the Andes the Conjuto Sierra Indian sets aside his Bolivian devil mask and watches dials and opens valves which send a branch of

Mother Amazon crashing no longer to the Atlantic, but to the Pacific.

No sooner had the shooting stopped in Korea than some 170 Bechtel men took the field and soon had 900 Koreans putting up the structures that would supply extra kilowatts to revive the country's economy. When Han River froze, modern methods were laid aside and Korean hand labor did much of the excavating and the debris was carried off on human backs. But before long the Koreans were squinting through transits, operating pile drivers, and driving the trucks and dozers.

The backbone of the force that built Tapline was comprised of Saudi Arabs and natives of the island of Bahrain. Since common labor was required in large numbers at the various work locations, unskilled help was generally hired directly from the Bedouin tribes at the nearest water hole. In the peak hauling period 291 Arab truck drivers were employed and 47 American truckers—a ratio of 6 to 1. At trucking, more than in any other single craft, one Arab could replace one American, and the descendants of camel drivers proved to be hot-rod gear-twisters. A yellow card with the workman's picture and thumbprint on one side and his proficiency rating on the other proved a great stimulus to the competitive spirit, of which the Arab has always had considerable. The inscription "Driver, Class A Kenworth truck, Convoy" was honor indeed.

Although in certain South American cities it is an ordinance that a passenger on a tramcar must wear at least one shoe, barefooted workers are a familiar sight throughout Latin America. In Venezuela, where a fast new highway connects Caracas with airport and seaport, veteran Em-Kayans trained 800 Venezuelans to run cats, shovels, scrapers, and dozers, to drill, and to shoot dynamite. So well did the Venezuelans learn the art of construction on the neighboring Orinoco project that the ratio of nationals to Yanks was 8½ to 1.

When M-K built Mocuzari Dam in northwestern Mexico, 7,500,000 yards of earth were moved by 650 Mexicans who were trained and supervised by 11 Yanks. There was a 651st Mexican who didn't need to be trained. He was a vaquero who'd practically been born in the saddle, and his job was to keep wild burros off the construction area. His steed was provided by the contractor and it was the only horse in the company's whole $30 million inventory. Papa Knudsen must have sighed in his grave.

Now and then a situation arises that defies the utilization of even key Americans. All must be left to the local personnel. In Arabia, M-K held a subcontract for public improvements, including highways and streets. All went well, with a few Yanks bossing Bedouin crews, until they neared the city of Mecca, which no infidel may enter. M-K had prepared for that one by scouting American colleges for a Moslem engineering student. In the University of Michigan they'd found Fouad Zaid, a Lebanese. "Fred" was sent to Boise for a sound briefing in street paving. Then he was flown to Arabia to run road crews and help to make Jiddah's and Mecca's streets look as much like Boise's as possible. When the workers neared Mecca, the American supervisors had to stand back and watch Fred and his crew pave their way over the horizon and onward. L. M. Greenleaf, boss of M-K's overseas activities, thinks the streets of the sacred city must have been paved all right, because no one complained. It's one M-K job that Harry and Ann Morrison haven't inspected personally.

Although the citizens of the U.S.A. who go abroad on these missions of construction are screened for a sense of responsibility and thoroughly coached about minding their own business and never, never whistling at an ankle or peeking behind an oriental veil, some of them do yield to the irresistible. When an overseas constructor received a commission to wire the king's palace at Riyadh, including the harem, there was no lack of American volunteers. One young man who put on electrician's overalls was by profession a photographer. He got in, but not with a camera, and came out with only his memories.

The Yanks not only teach crafts, they try hard to teach the nonmechanical races how to take care of their arms, legs, hides, and necks. This is often a hard thing to inculcate, especially in countries where human life has always been held of little value. When Atlas Constructors went to French Morocco to build air bases, a plan had to be laid out for utilizing, with safety, 12,000 Arabs, most of whom had never worked before in heavy construction. Safety engineers, by interpreter and gestures, told those greenhorn desert men how to take care of themselves around moving trucks and whirring wheels. And in spite of skirtlike burnooses and lifelong unfamiliarity with the difference, if any, between right- and left-handed monkey wrenches, the locals put in 3,500,000 man-hours with only six lost-time accidents.

Safety education was a major part of the program with a still farther away people, a race who throughout history have been rather bored by personal safety in any form. An Afghan would step straight off a jeep going 40 miles an hour, not realizing that it wasn't going at a camel's pace. T. Y. Johnston, as soon as he became manager on the Afghanistan project, worked out some fine safety talks and had them translated into the languages in vogue beyond Kojak Pass, and run off on tape recordings. What the Afghans would have refused to take from a foreign boss in person they absorbed with interest from a little talking box.

Minding his manners and suppressing any inclination to talk about "American know-how" or to pass hasty judgment upon what he finds, the American constructor, whether executive or mechanic, goes to the far corners of the earth. He is careful to respect the other fellow; to remember "This is *his* country," and to consider himself only a guest. Morrison observes: "It is an interesting and profitable experience to find that, in the many countries we have entered as strangers on the five foreign continents, business relationships are basically the same as here, that human beings think and feel alike behind their unfamiliar speech."

All in all, construction men and engineers seem to have done a far better job abroad, as cementers of good will, than many professional diplomats. They are close to the people, and their conversation, whatever the barriers of speech, is down-to-earth, helpful, and man-to-man.

Even though, as sometimes happens, the visitor from overseas is a trifle sensitive to his alien surroundings. Westinghouse sent a valve expert halfway around the globe to show some Afghans how to assemble equipment supplied by his firm. The expert completed his mission, and upon returning home reported: "They learned fast enough, but phew! how those wild men needed a bath!"

The Westinghouse expert was a full-blooded American Indian.

25

THE COLD WHITE FLAME OF VALOR

THE HEAVY construction industry might be expected to have its share of brave men, and it has. These are off on another tack completely from the daredevils, the show-offs, and the careless. Unassuming chaps, calm in the knowledge that they know their business or aware that they have been pinpointed for a task, they take great personal risks to save the job from disaster, or to rescue their mates in crisis.

There was Al Charron.

Al is of French-Canadian descent. Go back far enough and you'd probably find his ancestors pushing birch-bark canoes through the Great Lakes region in search of furs for Hudson's Bay Company, or fighting with Montcalm's forces at Quebec. But Al's canoe is an International TD-24 crawler-tractor with a bulldozer blade. A Canuck with long face-lines that bend easily into a quiet grin, and furrows about his thick brows from peering into dust and over snow, Al has the hands of a violinist on his tractor levers, and long practice has given him an acrobat's sense of balance along rocky brinks. He can be trusted to shove his load over the drop-off and get back before he follows it. He knows to the last ounce when to shove no farther, and how much power he has in reserve. He doesn't push his luck recklessly; he simply knows. Contractors value such men.

On this day, in May of '52, Al sat on his steel machine and looked up Kemano River canyon in northern British Columbia while his bosses, Mark Knight and Russ Madsen, talked a problem over. The walls of that jumbled canyon up ahead were sheeted with snow and the outjutting rocks dripped ice; springtime comes late up there. The floor of the canyon was an uptilt with snow 150 feet deep in places. Camp Kemano, down at the bottom of the gorge, was almost a vertical mile below and this present spot was known as Camp Nine. Above was Kildala Pass, and construction forces were trying to get up there and set up a camp on top, from which the road builders could work both ways—to Camp Kemano on this side and on the other side down to Kitimat, again at sea level, where the Alcan smelter was being erected. If the road builders waited for summer to melt the snow out of this canyon, they'd be in granite and could blast their road but would lose a whole construction year.

Russ and Mark were debating, Could a pioneering dozer get up there over the snow itself, breaking trail for more machines? But the snow in this gorge was given to avalanching. The slant was a thousand feet to the mile. In places the grade ran stiffer.

What the bosses were talking about, Al knew, concerned himself, his skill, his nerve, and the likelihood of a tractor's pound and jar starting snowslides. His tractor had once been hit by a two-ton rock and still had the dent of it, but he'd rather have taken another two-tonner than much of this white fluff, a cubic yard of which weighs half a ton, and of which there were yards beyond measure. It scarcely whispered as it moved, but it moved like a windshield wiper.

"Al," said Russ Madsen to the Canuck on the dozer, "have you led a good life?"

So here it came. The proposition. As to a good life—well, a man is never too sure.

"Because," Mark Knight slung in, "it looks like it's you to break that trail to where the angels are."

"Sure, oh sure," said Al Charron, once more squinting up those snow-ladders. He may have added other words which his ancestors used when Iroquois arrows whipped through the trees, or white water boomed.

Would the snow stay firm? "*Nous verrons ce que verrons,*" he muttered to his swamper. "We shall see what we shall see."

"It's up to you, Al, to decide whether you want to try. Purely voluntary," reminded one of the bosses.

Al shrugged. Mark and Russ knew their man.

Grub was loaded on the tractor, including a case of onion soup, a nourisher in which Al had great faith. Sleeping bags also went aboard, for this was to be a journey. A radio sending outfit, and cans of fuel. He squared the cat at *la belle dame sans merci,* the beautiful tauntress-mountain, and the swamper set out ahead on foot with a probing rod. Al rested his shoulders against the canopy supports; soon he would be half lying on his back.

The going was slow, requiring many zigzags. Al took an hour at an early point to climb 20 feet. No engineer would ever lay out a crazy road like this, but Al was looking for grades that he could cling to. Six miles to go. They were to require almost a week.

The men back at Camp Nine watched Al's progress for the next six days. If good wishes were 200-octane fuel, Al was already at the top. That first day he reached Glacier Creek, a chalky-white torrent that dashed from snow cavern to snow cavern. How to get across?

The helper with the probing rod located a possible way. A snow bridge. Alpinists walk nimbly over such spans. But what would happen if a tractor tried it?

The tracks of a tractor are designed to spread the weight. The pressure per square inch is very little. Not that a man would want a TD-24 to run over his hand or foot. But little, as pressures go. Al nosed his chariot out upon this white truss. It held. He was over. "*A la bonne heure!*" exulted Al. To his helper he shouted in affection, "*En avant,* you red-headed Swede!"

Beyond lay a desirable site for Camp Ten. Two days later it would be a camp for 120 men, for Mark Knight and Russ Madsen were organizing follow-up forces down below to take the trail Al was breaking; were lining up five tractors loaded with drill rigs, compressors, winches, and material for shelter roofs and walls. They waited only for Al to get well ahead where he wouldn't fall back upon them. But as far as the trail-blazing Al and his helper were concerned, when they made camp that night under a rock, they might as well have been on the moon. After supper—onion soup—Al leveled off the spot for his successors and made a few trail zigzags up ahead. Twilight at the north lasts late, in May.

A helicopter let some fuel down to them in cans next morning, and the *voyageur* again was off. Dislodged snow from above occasionally whispered past. Far below were the hemlocks and cedars of Kemano Valley, the cookhouses at the string of camps, the Quonset huts, and the construction headquarters down near the sea with their merry, neat office girls. Over on Mount DuBose, but below Al's altitude, was the airy cableway by which tunnel-drillers soared to work. Sometimes it was fog up here, but usually blinding sun.

Two or three days' battling brought scarcely any progress at all, for slipping back was frequent. At one point the tractor lost 300 feet in one hideous slide backward. Snow blindness finally got Al and he had to leave his machine and stumble down for aid. For one of the rare times in his life he decided that he'd had enough. Let somebody else have *la belle dame*. They sent a skinner up to take his place, but the relief man, upon closer look, concluded that the snow was in very present danger of melting, with mortal danger to the bulldozer, and declined the assignment. Not at current prices. Al heard about it, pushed the first-aiders out of his way, and strode back. He climbed aboard, lowered the blade to drop his center of gravity, shoved the steering levers into low range, crouched, and let 'er have it. The barrier snow slithered out of the way.

On the sixth day he was in the narrowest part of the ascent and he could see the notch ahead but here was almost no room for zigzagging. Then he stalled altogether. He got off and looked. There was just about one chance. The violinist-hands touched the levers lightly. He backed, braked his inside tracks, pivoted, hollered "*Ventre a terre!*" ("Belly down, and dig!"), and flung at that snowpile, hitting it at the angle he wanted. The engine roared, snow sprayed, Al's back almost shoved the seat canopy supports out of place, the obstacle gave, and he burst through to a broad floor of snow and was in the pass. The red-headed kid gave a yell of victory and leaped aboard. They hit the summit. Deep on the other side, a mile below through that cold, still air, were the roofs and mile-long smelter walls of Kitimat.

Al and his swamper grinned at each other, and allowed it had been a right coarse chore.

At noon on January 5, 1943, six persons boarded a two-engined Electra transport plane at Seattle, bound for Alaska. The roomy plane was one of the fleet of sixteen owned by the contractor who was building airfields, roads, and military installations along the northwest corner of the continent. The pilot of the plane was the chief of M-K's air fleet, a veteran of fifteen years at flirting with Alaska weather, named Harold Gillam. His passengers were Bob Gebo, M-K's general superintendent in Alaska; Percy Cutting, plane mechanic; Dewey W. Metzdorf, a six-foot-four 250-pounder, who owned and ran the Anchorage Hotel; Joe Tippets, radio expert with the Civil Aeronautics Administration; and Susan Batzer, who was on her way to Alaska to go to work for the CAA.

Hal checked his dials, took his signal from the tower, and was off, settling comfortably into the pilot's chair with his big fur coat handy for later on, if he needed it. Just now the air was balmy, with occasional sunshine spearing through the cloud. This flight out over Puget Sound and up over stepping-stone islets and fir-clad shores leading northward was pure pleasure for Hal Gillam, who was used to dodging peaks that hide behind Alaska's fog, rain, and snow. He'd flown this coast in everything from an open-cockpit plane to these big, cozy cabin jobs, and this Electra would be over Ketchikan, he promised his passengers, in about four hours and Anchorage in another four.

Behind him the passengers proceeded to get acquainted. Sue Batzer was from Idaho and this journey into the northland was a big adventure for her. She'd never been so far from home before, and besides seeing some new geography she

was going to play a part in the war effort of her country. Bob
Gebo, a thirty-six-year-old constructor, had been recently
promoted in the M-K ranks and he too felt the importance of
his new job. If Alaska and Harry Morrison wanted something
built, he'd build it. Percy Cutting, the aviation mechanic, had
just been on a Christmas visit with his wife and kids in California. Metzdorf, a real sourdough, had been in Alaska for
years, and nothing in sight here was new to him. Tippets,
the radio expert, was at home anywhere, especially on a plane.

Georgia Strait passed below. Mount Waddington's sharp
point appeared off to the right. Queen Charlotte Sound
opened out. Sue scribbled a description in her diary with a
well-manicured hand, then closed the book. Percy Cutting
and Joe Tippets talked airplane. Bob Gebo and the huge
Dewey Metzdorf chatted about the future of Alaska. Hal Gillam held the controls lightly and basked in the sunshine,
which now was complete. Soon the "banana coast" of Alaska
would present itself, with Ketchikan and its paper mills and
fishing fleets.

But over Dixon Strait, that wide entrance of the sea into
the inland passage, fog was seen streaming in. It looked like
a thousand rolling, tumbling Mount Saint Eliases, white and
silver and gold—a beautiful sight provided you were above it.
But Hal was due to drop down on Ketchikan for fuel. He spoke
to the tower over the radio phone. Visibility zero down there.
And soon he perceived that it was so. Town and valley were
in fog as dense as snowballs. He'd have to feel his way down
those feathery slopes and valleys of cloudland. Well, he'd
done that sort of thing a thousand times. . . .

For an instant the aerial direction beam faded. The plane
was passing directly over the control tower. Time to go down-
stairs. The floor was 11,000 feet below. Suddenly Hal sat for-

ward, every sensory nerve alert. His No. 2 motor was quitting.

He spoke of this, quietly, to the tower at Ketchikan. He'd try to find a beach, he said, and put the plane down on that. He'd landed on beaches before, on gravel bars, on snow slopes, even on glaciers. He would cruise a bit and watch for a hole in the fog. And he set himself to really handling this plane. He was losing altitude. One motor wasn't enough to keep him up at a safe level for hole-hunting.

This was the moment phantom fingers reached up and plucked the plane into a downdraft.

Gillam cut his remaining motor and strained for a glimpse of what lay below. All was fog: soft, yielding, implacable.

A tree branch caught the right wing, waltzed the machine around, and flung it with a crash into a "hard cloud"—an Alaskan mountain.

Joe Tippets was first to revive. He came out of nightmare to find that he was alive. He crawled from the wreck. Hal followed. They looked for the others. Sue Batzer was caught and pinned by the hand which had been writing her diary. Now it was jammed between seat and cabin wall. Dewey Metzdorf had a broken collarbone and some crushed ribs. Bob Gebo's leg was broken. Later, when rolling over, he broke his arm, too. Cutting was hurt inside, but like Tippets and Gillam, could crawl and help a little. They had to get Sue out. Gillam and Tippets managed to release her, but the sight of the smashed wrist and pulped fingers nearly finished them. Hal Gillam located some tarpaulins and spread them on the snow. It was drizzling. Sue's crushed hand kept on bleeding badly. They tried to stem the flow. Nothing could be done about her pain.

In the gray winter morning the men who had strength for it set about making a better camp. They burrowed into the

snow under one of the plane's crushed wings. It made a roof
of sorts. There was food in the plane, enough for a week if
used carefully. As events turned out, it was to be stretched
by the survivors for almost a month.

On the second day Sue Batzer died. The men laid her in
the snow, hoping the wolves wouldn't find her, and took council. They were on a tree-studded mountain and it would be
hard for rescue parties to spot; they'd better get down into a
valley where things were more open.

Gillam was in charge throughout. He was the least hurt,
and the best man by far at coping with the North. The five
men, one dragging a broken leg and dangling a broken arm,
one wincing under a broken collarbone, all suffering from
shock and cold and possible internal injuries, spent two days
toting their supplies down the mountain and into a hollow
where they hoped they would be seen. They made a brush
camp and built bonfires.

In Boise, in Seattle, in Anchorage, and at a dozen other
spots, all effort was thrown into organizing a search. Every
possible plane was hired. U. S. Coast Guard, U. S. Army Air
Force, Alaska Game Commission, Royal Canadian Air Force,
and a hundred fishing boats joined in. But there were thousands of square miles to be combed. No one knew whether
the plane had crashed on land or water. Weather was at its
worst.

As days passed, bringing no rescue to the campers, Gillam
decided to go forth and try to bring in help. He would follow
the mountains down until he came to the sea. There he might
find an Indian village. Taking only a pound of raisins and
two candy bars from the meager supply, fastening his parka
and latching snowshoes onto his booted feet, and shouldering
his light nylon parachute for a tarp, the forty-year-old six-

footer set out, promising to do everything he could and to do it as quickly as he could. Four injured men watched him go.

When more days passed, and no relief, Cutting and Tippets decided to set out too. Help had to be brought to the other men or they would die. The pair struck off, taking along a shotgun and a couple of shells and a few magnesium flares. They made painful work of it and they lost all track of days. They just plodded. A squirrel fell to the shotgun, and a crow. The game kept them alive. They came to the sea. At this point on the rocky edge of the continent there was no Indian village, no lodge or fire or any human sign. They found a few mussels and clams. Since the plane crashed, twenty-four days had passed.

On February 3 they were sighted by a patrol boat belonging to the Coast Guard. They'd tossed flares into their night fire and the tiny beacon was seen. Worn to rawhide shoestrings but still game and determined, the two were taken aboard and rushed to the Ketchikan hospital, wolfing Coast Guard grub as their vessel split the spray. Then, with nothing but first-aid treatment for their wounds, they set off with rescue parties in two planes to find their comrades.

Percy Cutting, in a plane driven by pilot Ray Renshaw of the Alaska Game Commission, first spotted the camp. Dewey Metzdorf, the man of huge stature, was down there on the snow, struggling about in a circle in order to be seen. He was so weak from starvation and the pain of broken bones that he could hardly drag. The plane set its pontoons down and the men aboard could scarcely refrain from crying at the scene they found: Metzdorf gamely standing there in welcome, Gebo lying under a tattered canvas shelter with broken bones and frozen feet. Water had rushed through the camp since Cutting last saw it, drowning out the fire, and the two men had been too weak to move. They hadn't had fire for almost a week. The icy water had soaked their blankets. They'd simply lain there, half frozen. Somehow they'd lasted through. When the pair were landed in Ketchikan, ten young Coast Guardsmen of the search and rescue crews were hospitalized with them, five with sprained ankles and five with frostbitten or frozen feet.

Hunt continued by land, air, and sea for the unreported Harold Gillam, who had left the camp for help four weeks before. Three hundred men were on the search. Three days after Cutting and Tippets were found, a shore party of Coast Guardsmen came upon the pilot's body on the beach of Boca de Quadra inlet.

His last act had been to remove his red underwear, hang it up for a signal, and affix his boots to the tips of high poles stuck in the snow. Then, every sacrifice made for his campmates, even to his body-cover in Alaskan winter, he had wrapped himself in his parachute and accepted fate.

Bob Gebo, many months later, had all his toes removed, but he globe-trots today for M-K in the Pacific, in a special $75 pair of shoes.

26

HOUSEKEEPING FOR A TITAN

WHEN British generals were chasing Rommel up and down North Africa, the fortunes of war favored the side that got supplies to the right place at the right time. Because they often ran out of gasoline and ammunition, the Allies had a hard time catching the desert fox. The experience heavy constructors have had in recent years at getting huge supplies to the spots where and when wanted led one of the private enterprisers to muse aloud one day, "If a good contractor had had charge of the logistics, Rommel would have been whipped sooner."

There's cause to believe he is right. Utah Construction Company getting all that stuff down to the shore of Peru, unreeling it from the ship and developing an empty beach into the nation's first port almost overnight; Steve Bechtel completing a 120,000-barrel-a-day oil refinery on one side of the world, Arabia, and a 35,000 BPDer on the other side, in Washington, together with a nickel smelter in Oregon, a 600,000-kilowatt steam plant in California, a 66,000-kilowatt plant in Utah, and a dam in the Sierra—and much, much more—all at the same time; H. W. Morrison with fourteen dams going up at once; Kaiser keeping his multitude of new plants rising—these amount to a wholesale exercise in logistics.

Up in Boise, Mark Robinson's office with its electric wheel-type card file is ready for any demand because it keeps track of every piece of important equipment, right down to when it had its last lick of paint.

The record-keeping procedure, quite different from Papa Knudsen's storage and procurement system of throwing the horse collars on a hook or buying a keg of bolts as he passed the general store, came into being in the early 1940s. Up to that time, major pieces of machinery had been numbered by a rough-and-ready method, if they weren't merely known by such monickers as Coal-Eater, Gear-Buster, or The Snorter. With the arrival of the big days the business machine salesmen moved in on Boise, and soon there were fifty-nine different classifications of the larger tools, such as excavators, tractors, trucks, and compressors, each with its own sequence of numbers. Today there are ninety classifications involving thousands of pieces of equipment. Numbers are painted on everything from a water pump up.

There's the slightly colossal item of spare parts. Earth-pushing contraptions can use more parts, and in a hurry, than you can shake an electronic punch-card at. Working minimums are kept on hand in warehouses in Boise, Los Angeles, Spokane, and up north at Anchorage. Some of the bins in Boise are in warehouses that once were hung with harnesses and horseshoes, and there is still a faint odor of ammonia about the sprockets, cams, and pistons that await call.

Much of M-K's overseas work is performed for governments that hold title to the equipment, but don't necessarily provide it. The company's buyers and stockkeepers at home are ready at the tinkle of a phone to supply a plane, a steamship, a typewriter ribbon, or a jackhammer. Purchasing in the United States, Alaska, and Mexico is handled from Boise, Seattle, and Los Angeles. A New York office shops for South American enterprises, a San Francisco office for the rest of the globe. Large projects also have their own purchasing agents. However, Boise usually buys the really big machines. In a single year the outfit may purchase as much as 600 pieces of "major" equipment—anything less than a $1,000 purchase being "minor"—and tossing it into the pool of machinery. The main corporation yard for this assemblage of dirt-disturbers, hill-flatteners, knoll-nudgers, and cranes with a boardinghouse reach is right where H. W. Morrison and Morris Knudsen started, on Broadway at the outskirts of the little inland city. The only thing that has been moved is the main gate. Mama Knudsen planted two linden trees as living pillars to the original gate, watering them with buckets that she toted from the Boise River, a ten-minute trudge. Now the trees have grown large, along with the firm. But Harry Morrison would as soon sever his own hand as cut down the two lindens, so diesel-powered behemoths have to come and go through another hole in the fence.

Professional and technical personnel is a prime department in all the construction outfits. At Kaiser Engineers steel files can flip out the record of an electrical engineer who knows Portuguese and Tagalog, or a cable rigger who speaks Arabic or Eskimo, and have him tagged as to his last and his next vacation, his salary, raises, and biographical details before the inquiring executive can hang up a phone. And somebody who thought he was in a rut finds himself on his way to New Zealand, Labrador, or Brazil, destiny in his hands and a promotion in his pocket. If he didn't get a job on the day he first dropped around, his application was kept on file. If he was likely material, needed at the moment, he'd been immediately sent to a prospective supervisor for further interviewing; if hired, he'd spent part of his first day in the personnel office getting a briefing and watching some sleek, wise young woman tabulate his work experience. When he came out of that day's session, he was a member of the team.

The housekeeping chore of a modern constructor includes various "memory departments." Kaiser has what it calls its Kaiser Engineers Office Services Department, which occupies three buildings and delivers anything from a pencil to the design print for a blast furnace. An alert guy named Gordon Smith, who probably forgets to mail his wife's letters even as you and I, has three hundred electronic memory machines, furlongs of steel files, a battery of nimble-fingered young women, and seventeen automobiles to help him whip out the drawings, reports, lists, letters, and office supplies that someone is always wanting several times a minute.

There's the matter of communications. When projects and men are scattered all over the earth, fast relaying of ideas and instructions is essential. Kaiser's organization is wired for talkfests. Twenty-five wire machines in the home town stutter out about four thousand messages a day over enough leased Western Union wire to belt the globe. It beats sending for the boy on the bicycle. Besides the Oakland wire center there are switching stations in New York, Los Angeles, New Orleans, Chicago, and Seattle, and direct wires from Oakland to eighty company offices and plants, hooked up to wire machines. The messages aren't compressed telegraphese either. Some are as long as a book. And somewhere in the files are carbon copies of all of them. What's more, there's always someone on duty who can actually find a particular carbon when wanted.

To keep the show on the road takes a lot of paper work and tape-snipping in Washington as well as at home. Bechtel's office two blocks from the White House handles company matters with the various executive departments and independent agencies of the Federal government; keeps in touch with Defense and Atomic Energy Commission; obtains passports and visas for the constantly shifting personnel of the Bechtel companies, and takes on every chore conceivable except lobbying and the solicitation of government business. Located at the fountainhead of statistics, this Washington mother's helper gathers economic and other reference data and feeds it back to the management. When Bechtel started building steam power plants in Korea, Art Shaw, the manager of the Washington office, found himself virtually a Bechtel ambassador to the Korean embassy. During the war years he was charged with obtaining allocations for strategic materials. Then followed the Saudi Arabian procurement program, the obtaining of allocations for steel for the Trans Mountain pipeline, and export licenses for the Aden refinery project. On practically all overseas jobs, export licenses from the Department of Commerce are involved. It's a branch of the "inside" work which keeps the projects going in the field. From his watchtower on Eye Street, M-K's Fred Huber watches similarly over the welfare of personnel floundering in the jungles of Washington, and Bechtel's George Coghlin steers his charges through the tall timber of New York.

In all the heavy construction headquarters there are the brightly lighted designing departments with tilted drawing boards on clean-smelling pine trestles. When a general layout plan has been worked out for a client, design groups turn

out the drawings which in turn lead to blueprints and specifications. Specialists in electrical, structural, piping, mechanical, and every other engineering field beetle their brows over
what's to emerge as a pipeline, a mill, or a mine, a refinery
or a chemical plant or a powerhouse, and the shirtsleeved
boys and sleeveless girls (yes, there are girl engineering designers too) leap into the act. The big constructors employ
such people by hundreds. The long-headed among them are
constantly coming up with new ideas. Big, daring ideas or
little, useful, money-saving, efficiency-producing ideas—they
are born by the dozens under the tubular white lights, and a
construction titan up in a plane or off on a distant continent
finds his personal reputation for brains duly enhanced.

At Kaiser's in Oakland there's Kaiser Engineers' schedul-
ing and process section, a segment of the statistics department. It prepares the engineering and construction schedules.
Such a schedule is a highly competent estimate of construction time—the time required for engineering design, for pro-
curing material and equipment, for shipping the stuff, and
for putting it up where wanted. The section works up each
month's activities into charts, drawings, photographs, and
summaries. When a job is done it has a complete historical
record, called a final report. Whether ever read or not, such
reports make a magnificent shelf of books and anybody walking by them has almost the feeling that he has walked the
length and felt the hidden energy of Grand Coulee Dam.

To watch over Kaiser Engineers' financial activities—accounts payable, payroll, cost, general accounting, and all that
headachy stuff—consumes the working time of 275 people in
seventeen field and branch offices and a main shop in Oakland using blond, brunette, and bald. The work is unspectac-

ular but Howard Tracy, comptroller, and Frank Bilotti, chief accountant, say it's fascinating.

There's the print room. Out of it come 180,000 square feet of blueprints a month. The shop guarantees immediate service. The files are endless. It takes nineteen winged-mercuries to produce and deliver the zillions of prints Kaiser activities require.

When negotiating with clients or preparing a bid, the key parties are the estimators. Upon their sharp pencils depends the fate of the business, and the requirement is that the pencils be sharp enough to win the job but not so sharp that the company will come home in a barrel. When estimating a completely designed project, the method is one of breaking it down into small parts and the small parts into yet smaller, and then determining the costs of labor, materials, and brainpower on each fraction. The drawing up of a human inventory follows—of what's needed from laborer to project manager. Into the ultimate total must also go an evaluation of intangibles, and that's where high art comes in. What's going to be the increase in materials costs? In wages? How much overtime? What beefs will arise? What weather will clamp down? What difficulties will develop that no man can foretelleth, but a bidder must calculateth? This, too, is a class of inside work that is said to be fascinating.

The construction companies all have first-rate libraries. Doris Lanctot, at Bechtel, will whip out an engineering magazine, a tome, or a brochure on anything from flying saucers to how to make Scotch, and is beyond surprise or defeat on any request. It is the same with the other outfits. Across the bay an average of one detailed research problem a day is taken on by research librarian Joe Russell and his assistant

Joan Hale—performed for any Kaiser engineer wanting special information.

And then, the legal departments. Their function is to keep hard-working constructors out of law courts; to see that bid documents and contracts have the Blackstone touch; to make sure that the fine-type legal boys who work for the clients aren't up to something roguish. All this is said to be not only fascinating but inspiring. Anyway, it's useful.

When you were still only a fast-rising vice-president of Evergreen Oil, Steve Bechtel was looking ahead and his fact-finding departments were holding the binoculars to his eyes. He perceived that you'd soon be in almost certain need of a new refinery.

Before they made you president of your company, a Bechtel "process group" was pondering the economics and geography of your area. Their voluntary study of the subject had grown into a shelf of reports and figures. Out in the field there were many first-rate sites for this refinery-to-be, but with the trunk and spurs of an oncoming pipeline considered, along with deep water, lay of land, transportation and access to markets, the hamlet of Leaping Salmon seemed a likely spot. At the time, Leaping Salmon consisted of a store, a filling station, and a fish wharf; it hadn't leaped very far as yet. The study went into the files.

A refinery is one of the complicated mechanisms of this technical age. Its designers have to take into account the types and variety and characteristics of your raw material; what you intend to make of it and in what proportions; what the markets want now and what they will want tomorrow. Your company engineers unquestionably can cope with many or most of them. You can stiffen your organization with more talent and handle them all. But that would tie up your staff to the exclusion of other pressing matters. Learning that Bechtel's people have something to suggest, you invite them in.

The engineers bring with them a whole refinery in miniature. It's in a case about 3 by 2½ feet. The contents of the case look like a child's structural toy set. About two hundred small parts are packed neatly. They are accurately made to scale, of wood with metal base plates and connections. As a single section of a catalytic tower may be over 100 feet in height and weigh 100 tons, and isn't easy to move around (though Bechtel moved one a thousand miles), its prototype in reduced scale is handier for office-desk purposes. Out they come, miniature pressure vessels and supports, pumps and drivers, heat exchange facilities, stripping columns, debutanizers, desulfurizers, depropanizers, compressor house and control house, and all the rest. You begin to see your refinery rise on your conference table.

This portable take-down and put-up refinery was designed and made under the direction of Fred W. Meyer, Bechtel vice-president in charge of refinery engineering; Russell G. Johnson, chief engineer; and A. Glenn Harding, assistant chief engineer. The tools required in building the model before your eyes are pliers and a screwdriver. The kid in you is delighted by this scale model of an experienced refinery designer's suggestion. And the president in you has a whale of a time rearranging, tearing down, building up. But you consider, thoughtfully and carefully, what the model implies. These men have worked on about one hundred oil and chemical plants in the past nine years, all the way from carrying out a client's specifications to taking the job over from the ground up. They can save you months of time, and perhaps millions in money. So you size up recommendations and you compare alternatives. You visualize the ultimate plant as if you were walking through it. Later when the preliminary decisions have been made, a more elaborate model can be built to a larger scale, with much of the elaborate piping detail included.

Bechtel's process group, working in San Francisco and in the field, operates under a solid-chinned engineer named Gordon Zimmerman and they are the shock troops of the Bechtel refinery division, for they go into action whenever the boss has an idea, and before the contract is signed. It's all a part of the inside work which makes a constructor's outside work possible. What Bechtel does for refineries he also does for chemical plants, power plants, and other industries.

So, at Leaping Salmon on the seacoast or out on the prairies of America, the farmer stops his tractor to look at them— silvery towers and cylinders and spheres, batteries of stacks and grotesquely graceful parabolas of pipe. In the Middle East the camel driver or jeep driver halts to view the domes and minarets of industry—Bechtel-built refineries at Aden, Ras Tanura, Bahrain, Lebanon. The Neapolitan fisherman, homing by way of the smoke of Vesuvius, has a new beacon to steer by and it gleams by day and shines with uncounted lamps by night—that new refinery.

In a single year Bechtel has had fifteen refinery jobs under construction. Good staff work on the inside makes such a variety of special engineering or construction feats possible. The world has become Steve's office table; a big chunk of the petroleum, steam power and atomic power industries, his erector set.

In go penstocks for Chief Joseph's mighty powerhouse.

Above, the old way, frequently still used, and below, the new.

One good dozer holds another in Oregon.

Nudging rock for Donnells Dam in Sierra Nevada.

Knocking the U. S. Continental Divide down to size.

Beasts of burden: at Kajakai (Afghanistan) dam site, above, while below is a modern earth hauler.

Iron ore for a Venezuelan ore railroad bed.

"What drives them on?" The challenge of vistas like this at Hoover — still No. 1 for height — the Earth Changers can never resist.

27

WHAT DRIVES THEM ON?

ONE DAY well before the desert-chilly hour of sunrise, engineers and other observers for a dozen electric utility companies ducked into holes in the ground and stayed there while the seconds ticked. They had come to a sagebrush and salt-strewn spot in Nevada to find out something important to their companies. The utilities, which knew much about the awfulness of the power in a hurricane, flood, ice storm, or earthquake, wanted to know what would happen to their power lines and stations, and to homes in general, come a nuclear blast. Bechtel had designed and built a "Doomstown" for the Atomic Energy Commission, to provide a practical answer.

The AEC's atomic device was mounted on a 500-foot steel tower. At five-ten the switch was tossed and the soft pearly dawn of the desert went white and orange.

The Bechtel organization has been wading about in nuclear engineering right up to its slide-rule pockets, before and since.

The atom is joining coal, petroleum, and falling water as a prime source of industrial energy. Arco in Idaho, and various pilot plants, have sprung in part from Bechtel conference rooms and drafting rooms into stone and steel. Projects now on the drawing boards are many. Says Steve, "The Bechtel interests are keenly interested in the future of nuclear power for industry and to that end are spending probably fifty per cent of their forward thinking in the power field."

For nothing since the invention of the steam engine has stirred men's minds as has the development of nuclear atomic energy. In the dozen years since Hiroshima, weapons have found two other mainstreams of development flowing from the harnessed, or unharnessed, atom. These are isotopes and electric power generation. Bechtel Corporation has been affiliated with weapons and electric power generation as participant, engineer, and constructor.

The 180,000-kilowatt Dresden Nuclear Power Station is rising to completion 50 miles southwest of Chicago. General Electric Company is the prime contractor for Commonwealth Edison Company, the owner and operator; Bechtel Corporation is the engineer-constructor for General Electric, performing all construction and design except the nuclear package. Seven utilities and Bechtel sponsored the research and development expense through Nuclear Power Group, Inc. Dresden, to be completed by 1960, will be the first and the major all-nuclear plant in the U.S. to be financed by private capital.

In the opinion of a national study panel assembled under provisions of the Atomic Energy Act, 15 per cent of all new power-generating facilities in the United States will be nuclear by 1965, 45 per cent by 1970 and 65 per cent by 1980. Strange are the shapes of buildings rising to house these activities; strange are the shapes of things to come. But it is no longer in the lap of tomorrow. It is virtually here, at least for those countries where coal and oil costs are excessive or where there is the cold fear of another cutting off of supplies through Suez.

Most of the constructors who evolved from Hoover Dam are hipdeep in atoms, and so are the many, including some very large ones, whom this book does not attempt to cover. The era which opened on the sands of Alamogordo on July 16, 1945, shook up drawing boards and earth-moving equipment far beyond the reach of that flash of light. Years after Hanford was first erected, Kaiser Engineers are still some of the keepers of its awesome secrets, and anybody who went up there for a job on an expansion project gave up more than his fingerprints. His history and his mental innards were held upside down, shaken well, and thoroughly X-rayed. If he was very, very trustworthy he got a badge and could pass the gates. And that's about all that was known about it, except that Kaiser had 250 engineers and heavy thinkers up there, along with 6,000 workmen, who went in through the gates with transits, levels, chains, rods, slide rules, and tool kits, and came out tight-lipped, with starry looks in their eyes.

Hanford has grown since war days. Its reservation is still 600 square miles, half the size of Rhode Island, and to its original $350 million worth of plant facilities, $550 million more have been or are being added. The $110 million project that went to Kaiser Engineers in 1952 has had Kaiser executives shuttling back and forth ever since.

In addition to this renewed dive into atoms, Kaiser people are deep in the study of nuclear power for industry. For a pound of fissionable uranium has the potential energy of 2,600,000 pounds of coal and can be made to "breed" additional fuel. It can spin lots of wheels. In 1954 Kaiser Engineers set up a special division to keep abreast of developments. The well-staffed group works at design and engineering of nuclear processes, power reactors, and the construction that they imply, and upon the application of nuclear technology to chemistry and metallurgy. At Idaho Falls experimental test facilities are being built for AEC of interest to aircraft propulsion.

The titans who emerged from the era of New Deal spending in the '30s, war in the '40s, and private works in the '50s are furiously busy. Time tries to slow them down, with no success. What drives them on? The profit motive? They long since "got theirs." The urgency of providing for heirs? Morrison has no children; for the others, the future is by now as secure as a well-built dam. The answer seems to be that these men can't stop building and don't want to. Aside from a deep sense of responsibility toward the organizations they have created, they love the going.

The writers of this chronicle were with Harry and Ann Morrison, firing at the earth mover the question, "What drives you on?" when H.W. was called from the room. He came back, snatched his wife up, kissed her, did a small jig, and exulted, "Well, we won it! The Tri-County Dam."

He'd given the answer, this old-time driver of Frog and Toad, this pusher of the Model T in the long ago, now past seventy with works reaching into billions. What keeps him at it is sheer love of building, and the fun of the game.

To this, one of Morrison's right-hand men adds, "We think H.W.'s two driving impulses have been and are to level out contracting hazards by diversified risk-spreading, and to build an organization to survive him. Both are accomplished."

Another hand says of his boss, "He keeps telling us that we must make a profit, make a profit, but I think that's just so we won't make a loss." In other words, stay in business.

In Steve Bechtel the observer cannot help noting a deep

sense of citizenship and of satisfaction in being one of the bull wheels of private enterprise. Steve can walk with governments, but he infinitely prefers to walk and talk with the oil men, the chemical men, the industrialists who represent his own type of rugged individualism in the American tradition. As long as some projects are too big and complex for private purses, or are tied in with national defense, Steve Bechtel will build for the government, but the business firms that operate for business motives are his choice.

Henry J. Kaiser seems to feel closer now than his contemporaries do to being free for a long-postponed hour in the sun. He went to Hawaii for a sojourn. But the soft winds, lush landscape, and pleasant sea didn't cause Henry J. to become a lotus eater; they simply stirred up the builder in him. Oahu isle is so beautiful—and so small. Only 90 miles around, in the middle of all this ocean. Well, why not make Oahu larger?

So the earth changer was at it again. He told a reporter, "When I was twenty-two I decided Florida would never develop a tourist business and passed up a chance to be in on the ground floor there. Then I went on to figure that Palm Springs and Las Vegas were desert sand traps and always would be. I don't want to miss the boat again." He picked up an old hotel, the Niumalu, just off the center of Waikiki district, bought a nearby belt of real estate, and began to visualize how that sandy loam would blossom when watered with $20 million. (Some say that his sights are set on $120 million.) The dredges were summoned, and the clamshells and draglines. With a Los Angeles builder, Fritz Burns, he pulled down the hotel and put up Hawaiian Village—the plushest array of grass shacks, complete with modern plumbing and blue lagoons, yet to be seen in the South Seas. Over from the little Oahu village of Laie were fetched a bunch of Samoan thatch

weavers, with instructions to build roofs which would make
Hawaii look as visitors thought it ought to look. Hawaiian Village was built in ninety days; $14 million worth of improve-
ments in general went in; Kaiser announced a five-year plan
of glamorous hotels for the island chain; and old-timers
groaned, "We're being Kaiserized!" Certainly nothing like it
had happened since Pearl Harbor or, before that, the far-off
day when the missionaries first brought New England Mother
Hubbards to throw around the sun-kissed nakedness of the
Hawaiian Polynesians. At age seventy-four the son of German
immigrants looked about at his growing handiwork, and told
the Islanders, "What you can see here now is about seven
per cent of what will be built." Three or four new hotels with
2,000 more rooms are included in Henry J.'s plan.

And in Oakland the plan was announced for a $35 million
Kaiser Center, a new headquarters building. A many-storied
curve of glass and aluminum, to stand at the head of Lake
Merritt and give a crown of splendor to the Kaiser empire.

Fortunately for these and the other earth changers, there
are big potential challenges still ahead. Canals to be cut at
Nicaragua and across the neck of Malay Peninsula. A diversion of the Yukon River at its sources under Taku Glacier on
the Alaskan plateau of high lakes, and the dropping of its
thunders through penstocks to generators at Skagway, half a
mile below.

The Colorado River is beginning to look like a ladder of
dams at its lower end, and the rungs will continue. The rivers
of the West will not be permitted to flow wastefully away to
the sea much longer. Not with Southern California clamoring
for a drink. Mighty Columbia, which rolls out into the Pacific
in volume, may find that it too has a date with Los Angeles.
There'll be ranges to cross with siphons, but the Southwest

is in a water vacuum and its struggles are intense. Still, this
one is a concept to stagger the imagination. About like leading the Mississippi from St. Louis to Savannah, over several
ranges each twice the height of the Appalachians.

Bill Waste of Bechtel puts it, "Nothing is too big or costly
to dream about, or to study seriously. This [Columbia] proposal involves well over a thousand miles in distance and a
volume of water upwards of twenty million acre-feet annually. The distance is more than three times that over which
water is now being moved to Los Angeles, and the quantity
is about twenty times the capacity of the Colorado River
Aqueduct. Whether or not the estimated cost of five billion
is justified—granting that precedent exists for overcoming
physical obstacles—is an immediate question. But somehow—
sometime—if the need exists, the result will be accomplished
even though today it appears possible only as a joint venture
of King Midas and Paul Bunyan."

Allen Christensen of Utah Construction feels that the making and lifting of pure water from the inexhaustible oceans
is one of the certain great engineering undertakings of the
future.

Other developments, assured or likely:

Vast revision of the nation's highways. Huge landing fields
and maintenance bases, for heavy round-the-world and trans-
oceanic aircraft, miles away from metropolitan centers, with
feeder airports and landing strips in city centers or on building tops. Residential tracts and housing projects 50 to 150
miles from cities, with workers transported back and forth by
high-speed surface and air transportation in a matter of minutes. The linking of power lines to create a national hookup
for power distribution throughout the nation. Reclamation of
arid lands to an extent undreamed of, and development of
inland waterways. Gas pipelines of diameters and lengths un-

heard of. Conveyor tubes for moving dairy products, meats, and other perishable foods to distribution points throughout given metropolitan areas. The relocation of whole industries underground for military and economic reasons. The reduction of coal to semiliquid or pulverized form for movement through pipelines. (This is a practical reality now and the idea may also be applied to plastics and other things which can be rendered liquid and pumped along.)

A favorite Steve Bechtel dream may never come true because of political roadblocks. But it's one to which Steve has given much thought and study: a big-inch gas pipeline west and northwest from the oil fields of the Middle East into and across western Europe. Such a pipeline would make over the economies of the coal-poor countries. New manufacturing centers would develop and the map of Europe would be in for changes no mind can foresee. The physical difficulties, provided the gas is in the ground, are not engineeringly insurmountable; this is the considered opinion of the men who crossed the Rockies and the sands of Arabia with their big-inch lines.

The eradication of smog is a big-scale engineering problem that the overgrown cities of the country will have to solve or be doomed.

Harry Morrison, who never lets his thinking stray too far from the contract in hand and the bidding just ahead, considers the St. Lawrence Seaway one of the outstanding developments in modern construction history. This international joint venture, materializing the dreams of a century by joining North America's Great Lakes with the Atlantic, will open interior cities and rivers to ocean-going ships. It is such a vast project that almost the whole roster of major North American contractors are at work on it.

The titans call for help and the engineers and construction stiffs respond, though the work may be right at home or at the ends of the earth. For many there is flavor and savor to far-off places. A cat skinner wouldn't admit it, insisting that "A job's a job, wherever it is," but the very sound of some place names causes lotus blossoms to toss their perfume and temple bells to sing. The plainest, flattest piece of highway, such as Charley Buck of M-K is building in Iraq—straight up the level Tigris-Euphrates Valley for Amarah, with a rise of only 7½ feet in 75 miles—takes on a rosy-purple hue when mention is made that it starts at Basra, legendary port of Sinbad the Sailor; passes the junction of the rivers where a sign says GARDEN OF EDEN—and where more likely?—leaves ancient Ur of the Chaldees off to the left, the mountains of Iran on the right, and drives to Amarah en route to Baghdad. With Babylon just off the path and Nineveh up the line a bit farther. What matter if Baghdad, up the road beyond the present M-K contracts, is a modern city and no one remembers where the palace of Caliph Haroun al Raschid used to be? The main stem is Raschid Street and this is still *Arabian Nights* country and a man feels it even when jouncing on a bulldozer. Every time the blade drops in Iraq, it pushes through soil that once was Sumaria, Chaldea, Babylonia. Sometimes while plowing out licorice-root bushes it turns up jugs and pitchers and the bones of slaves or kings.

At the Erlander home in the hills beyond San Francisco Bay a reunion of old friends and their families is being held. Olof wears the apron and stabs with the barbecue fork and Tooe does the welcoming. "Is it lobscouse we eat today, us Norvegs?" asks Abe Kanterwitz, who has grown plump with prosperity. Lloyd & Kanterwitz, in which he is a silent partner, has made him a millionaire.

"Mulligan, I hope," interjects Tom Quinn. Burly Tom is not the active man he was at Hoover Dam. Too much tunnel and concrete work. He leans on a heavy cane.

"It'll be steaks, folks, in this cookhouse," informs Olof. He beams through the charcoal smoke. It is good to see Lloyds and Kanterwitzes, Quinns and Erlanders, gathered again.

Kate Quinn, big and hearty, and in a dress of dollar-size polka dots, cries, "All we need is a dust storm! Do you remember the three-bucketer that we had when you had your fourth baby, Tooe?"

"I and Abe have news for you," announced Mrs. Kanterwitz.

"Mama! That you should spring it on me this way!" exclaims Abe.

"It's not that, Abraham Kanterwitz, and you know it. It's that Lew Lloyd and our Jacob have won a new contract. To bridge the Bosporus!"

Abe smiles widely. "From Europe all the way to Asia, this bridge our boys will build. How we operate! Next time, a bridge from Tokyo to San Francisco."

It's fine to have the boys successful, thinks Olof. But now Molly and her children will be gone away off to Turkey for several years. Always it's away somewhere, with these construction people.

"I have a letter from our son Trygvasson," Tooe tells proudly, drawing it from her bosom. "He is with Kaiser in Spokane. Hear what he says.

"*'Dear Mom and Dad: This is really something to see. An aluminum rolling mill layout is actually a great big job shop, as every customer wants something just a little bit different. Forty different alloys and tempers at least, in thicknesses from* *six-thousandths of an inch to 3 inches, and widths half an inch to 80 inches in coils and sheets, are pouring out of here at a rate of 36 million pounds in a month. Cranes overhead go screaming across the building with 5,000-pound ingots swinging underneath. The crash of 16-inch ingot hitting the initial breakdown mill and coming out the other side seconds later, only 7 inches thick—rolled out like pie crust, in exactly the same way—the roar of the remelt furnaces when the door opens and the charge goes in, and finally the rattle of the freight cars as over a million pounds a day ship out the back door—that's what I live in all day, and I love it. Fifty-three acres under one roof and the activity never slowing, twenty-one shifts a week. Across the street is the Division of Metallurgical Research where even the janitors have doctor's degrees—I don't think there is a man in there over forty—they say, "Gentlemen, our ultimate aim is to be able to make an airplane out of one piece of aluminum." Across the river is one of our smaller reduction plants, Mead, where fifty lines of pots shoot electricity through to make aluminum. It runs up an electricity bill of $550,000 a month. Here too is feverish activity, but there still isn't enough aluminum to satisfy the market and we are building and building more capacity, bigger equipment, even though it will be outdated by the time it can produce. Everybody seems to want the stuff for baby rattles and bombers and furniture and Christmas wrappings and electric wire and barnyard roofs. . . .'"*

It's America, Olof reminds himself. It's America at vork. All our children are at vork. It's a great country.

"All right, folks!" he calls, spearing up the sizzling steaks to the platter Art Lloyd is holding. "Plenty to eat now—this isn't Tar Town. Pull up and reach!"

BIBLIOGRAPHY

Colley, George S., Jr., *Manila, Kunching and Return, 1944–45.* Privately printed, San Francisco, 1946.

Fanning, Leonard M., *Foreign Oil and the Free World.* McGraw-Hill Book Company, 1954.

Finnie, Richard, *Canol, The Sub-Arctic Pipeline and Refinery Project.* Privately printed, San Francisco, 1945.

Ingram, Robert L., *A Builder and His Family.* Privately printed, San Francisco, 1949.

Morrison, Ann, *Those Were the Days, Diary of Ann Morrison.* Em-Kayan Press, Boise, Idaho, 1951.

Pettitt, George A., *So Boulder Dam Was Built.* The Six Companies, Inc., 1935.

Sundborg, George, *Hail Columbia, The Thirty-Year Struggle for Grand Coulee Dam.* The Macmillan Company, 1954.

Woodbury, David O., *Builders for Battle.* E. P. Dutton & Company, 1946.

Fortune; engineering periodicals; preliminary and progress reports; publications of the companies.

Much of this book has been gathered from construction men in the field.

INDEX

Mohammed Zahir Shah, 125, 126, 128
Moore, Charles, E., 82
Moraga project, 107–8
Moreell, Ben, 77, 78, 83
Moreell's bases. *See* Pacific island naval bases
Morrison, Ann, 36, 39–43, 44–45, 47–49, 50, 53, 56, 94, 233, 265, 292
Morrison, H. W. (Harry), 18–19, 20, 25, 31, 36, 37–49, 50–53, 70, 76, 80, 87, 136, 201, 217, 233–34, 240, 249, 253, 265, 267, 279–80, 292, 296
Morrison-Knudsen Construction Co., 25, 32, 38, 52–56, 68, 71, 76, 79, 87, 93, 101, 112, 117–23, 126, 131–38, 144, 156, 179, 182, 193, 198, 242, 244, 264, 273, 280, 297; overseas operations, 53–54; subsidiaries, 55, 128
Morrison-Knudsen International, Inc., 55, 146, 147
Mototan-Mene Grande highway, 98
Mountain of the Magnet, 109, 110–11
Mt. Isa Mines, Ltd., 209
Munson, J. G., 181, 182

National Associated General Contractors of America, 31
Nations, Paul, 51
Navajo Indian Reservation, N.M., 108
Nechako River, 195, 196, 205
Nejd, 139, 140, 144, 147; construction, 54
New York City, 7, 21, 73, 106
New Zealand, 55; construction, 54
Ney, Carl M., 146–47
Niagara River pipelines, 249–50
Nichols, Earl, 183
Northwestern Pacific Railroad, 24, 27
Nuclear engineering, 289–92
Nuclear Power Group, Inc., 290
NWP. *See* Northwestern Pacific Railroad

Oahu, 75, 77, 78, 79, 80, 244, 293–94
Oetjen, Otto, 137
Ohliger, Floyd, 143

Oil, 27, 139–45, 232–33. *See also* Petroleum
Okinawa, 82
Oklahoma Contracting Co., 101
Oliver Iron Mining Co., 181
Olson, Harry, 131
O'Neill, Bill, 141, 142, 178
Open-pit mining, 24
Operation Ice Cube, 54
Oppenheim, Lou, 236
Ordway, A. B., 31, 217–18
Oregon Short Line Railroad, 23, 24
Orinoco Mining Co., 182
Orinoco River, 43, 180, 181, 187
Oroville, Cal., 24; rock plant, 31
O'Shaughnessy Dam, 24, 251
Oxus River, 125

Pacific Bridge Co., 33, 67, 68, 71, 91, 93
Pacific Coast, 93, 99
Pacific Gas & Electric Co., 29, 101
Pacific island naval bases: appropriation, 78; construction, 78–80; contract, 78; contractors, 83; cost, 77
Paine, Karl, 38–39, 46, 47
Pakistan, 55, 127, 131, 132; construction, 115–16
Palmer, Silas, 29
Palmyra Island, 77, 78
Panama Canal, Miraflores Lock, 99
Panic of 1890's, 23, 26
Parker Dam, 67, 98, 106
Parsons, Ralph M., 97
Pastor, Justo, 109
Peace River, 101
Pearl Harbor, 76, 78, 79, 84, 191
Perini, B., & Sons, 112, 113, 210
Perini, Lou, 52
Permanente Cement Co., 91–92, 217, 221
Permanente Metals, 100
Persian Gulf, 139, 140, 141, 144, 146, 147
Peru, 55, 105, 106, 109–12
Peruvian ore, 109–12
Petroleum: pipelines, 101–2; transport and refining, 97–99. *See also* Oil
Philippines, 77, 83, 84